Supportive Music Therapy for Grief and Loss

A Practical Handbook for Professionals

Ruth Bright

Registered Music Therapist (Australia)
Member of the Order of Australia

MMB MUSIC, INC.

SUPPORTIVE ECLECTIC MUSIC THERAPY FOR GRIEF AND LOSS

A Practical Handbook for Professionals

Ruth Bright, RMT (Australia), Member of the Order of Australia

Editor: James H. Heine
Typography: Gary K. Lee
Printer: Bookmasters, Mansfield, Ohio
First Printing: October 2002
ISBN: 1-58106-027-0
Printed in USA

For information and catalogs, contact:

MMB Music, Inc.
Contemporary Arts Building
3526 Washington Avenue
Saint Louis, MO 63103-1019 USA

Phone: 314 531-9635; 800 543-3771 (USA/Canada)
Fax: 314 531-8384
E-mail: info@mmbmusic.com
Web site: http://www.mmbmusic.com

Contents

Foreword
W. Walter Menninger, MD

Although I am sure it is not the author's intention, reading this treatise prompts a feeling of envy—envy for the author's broad understanding of human motivation and behavior; envy for the author's empathy and intuitive skills; envy for the author's capacity to integrate music in all its forms to reach troubled persons and thereby enhance their state of mind and their capacity to adapt.

This is an extraordinary book, written clearly with a minimum of jargon and a maximum of explanation to assist the reader in the understanding of theory and practice. While the book is specifically focused toward music therapists, all practitioners could be enhanced by the book's discussion of the processes underlying grief and methods for dealing with the emotional challenges associated with loss. The author facilitates the reader's understanding through poignant case illustrations that include an articulation of the therapist's thinking processes during the therapeutic encounter.

With each chapter we are presented with aims and learning objectives which are elaborated in considerable detail. The author provides an outline of the specific steps and critical elements to be undertaken in diagnostic and therapeutic sessions with the patient. An effective summation closes the chapter.

Theoretical formulations are carefully explained and well annotated, and procedures are outlined in a step-by-step manner. The subtle differences of addressing grief therapy in different contexts are detailed. The author does a superb job of integrating insight and understanding of grief processes with the appropriate therapeutic interventions. She also acknowledges that as therapists we are not always successful in our work.

After reading this work I could only wish that music therapists of the talent, scope and sensitivity of the author were widely available. Clearly, the utilization of a wide range of musical experiences can provide an avenue to reach patients struggling with loss and grief. The challenge is to put all of the pieces together, and this work goes a long way toward helping music therapists be better prepared to do that.

Preface

This is a practical handbook with a theoretical substratum, rather than a theoretical treatise with occasional ideas for action. It provides guidance on the use of music therapy in counseling and psychotherapy for the broad issues of grief and loss in the context of individual work with a variety of populations. Although the main focus of the book is on grief resolution, the approach is applicable to most human predicaments, where grief, in one way or another, is almost universal.

The book is personal and draws on many examples of different approaches and methods that proved effective with different people and different problems. For some, these involved major changes, but for others the work chiefly consisted of helping the person cope with what was certainly immutable and seemed unendurable. I have written in a conversational style, not as an academic text but as if giving a seminar face-to-face, with personal comments to enrich and emphasize the points that are made.

Because of its eclectic nature, the book has been complex to arrange. I could not, for example, have a chapter exclusively on the insight-based approach since this is almost invariably used in conjunction with other methods. The same is true for counseling methods and cognitive behavioral approaches—only rarely is one approach used in isolation. The book is therefore arranged with short sections describing music therapy approaches for each area of difficulty, and with discussion and suggestions how to select and use different approaches. Vignettes illustrate these. These sections do overlap on occasion—lives cannot be neatly put into the folders of a filing system! I hope cross-references and the index will enable the reader to track down whatever theme is sought.

The term supportive in the book title does not mean that we offer only an emotional crutch, important as this can be. One also needs support as one recognizes the need to change, and especially as one starts to put the necessary changes into effect.

I hope this book avoids "fossilizing" any one method or philosophy and that it will lead other music therapists to work in a supportive, eclectic approach to human need.

Introduction

Music Therapy for Grief
A Personal Viewpoint

Over the four decades of my work in music therapy I have developed a personal philosophical approach to meeting the needs of troubled individuals. It is not through a conscious intention to "do my own thing," nor to claim uniqueness, but a consequence of seeing (and to some extent sharing) the distress of so many people and of coming to realize that different individuals with different problems need different approaches if change is to take place. Interestingly, I have also found that the concept of change has a different meaning for different people. For one person it may mean altering one's way of living and thinking, but to another the change may be from despair to positive acceptance of strategies to deal with inescapable problems.

The years have also brought a wider concept of grief so that this is now perceived as permeating the lives of many who do not, in the eyes of the world, seem to have suffered any major loss. From this has grown a wider understanding of who needs help—and why—and the development of greater skills in providing that help.

What Induces Grief?

In the early days of grief counseling, grief was associated with death and dying (Hinton, 1967; Kubler Ross, 1974). Today, however, we recognize grief as a response to any significant loss, realizing also that a loss that may be significant to one person can be trivial to another.

We grieve over many experiences and events. Sometimes we do not recognize or describe our responses as grieving because that often suggests crying, sighing, and other obvious indications of sadness. But grief is more than sadness. It can include anger, humiliation, feelings of depression, disbelief, relief of tension after the ending of a difficult relationship, and many other emotions. Therapists may also see a physical transformation (somatization) of grief into bodily symptoms. Clients may be grieving about:

- approaching death;
- bereavement by death;
- genetic impairment so that childbearing is unwise;
- birth of a child with a genetically caused impairment;
- chronic acquired illness or disability;
- relationship breakdown resulting from illness, disability, or another cause;
- fear resulting from diagnosis of a major disorder of body or mind;
- loss of employment;
- poverty;
- diagnosis of dementia;
- stigmatization—from psychiatric disorder or acquired disability, from being a member of a minority group, from political repression;
- change of role due to illness or acquired disability (including dementia) in the client or a significant other;
- birth of a child with impairment that presages long-term handicap and high support needs, dread for the future in the parents, who fear their own old age when they will no longer be able to provide support;
- loss of expectation as a result of any of the losses listed above.

No one therapist can be fully informed about all of these, but we need to be aware of the wide implications of illness and disability, aware too of the sometimes paradoxical responses to loss. Grief is not always "on show." It may be hidden under substance abuse or a veneer of brisk competence, or it may be obscured by denial, depression, or humor.

Why Do People Need Help?

Although one sometimes wonders what "normal grief" really consists of, most of us face losses of many kinds throughout our lives, and most of us are able to cope with them fairly adequately, given time and a healthy attitude to the loss and the relationships that preceded that loss. But not everyone can do that. Some people need help coping with their losses. In working with the people who have been referred to me, I have found that their obstacles to grief resolution fit into two main categories:

- Matters that originate within the person, usually because of poor self-image—difficulties in acknowledging or expressing feelings; inability to think logically and objectively about life events; feelings of guilt, even when this is unwarranted; difficulties with intimacy, so that it is hard to talk about difficult matters; fear of rejection or disapproval

- Matters that originate in the attitudes of others—derogatory attitudes toward the client for no justifiable reason; living in poverty and social isolation; being the victim of manipulation of circumstances or attitudes (this includes political, religious, or minority-group repression); the grief is not "respectable," is socially forbidden (disenfranchised); childhood prohibition of anger, grief, or any strong emotion; unhealthy and destructive role models in human relationships; destructive defense mechanisms (Vaillant, 1977)

All these external factors reduce the capacity to cope with difficulties. They are further complicated when there is a psychiatric or other disorder, or where there is brain impairment from whatever cause. For example:

- Psychotic illness or a delusional belief system that is out of touch with reality
- Depressive illness that leads the survivor of the loss (whether death, separation, unemployment, or other) to see the fault as entirely personal, perhaps to the extent of feeling that suicide is necessary
- Personality disorder or other disorder that leads to an inappropriate projection of blame onto someone else
- Brain impairment from substance abuse, trauma, illness, or acquired disability
- Intercurrent illness or weakness
- Innate physical or intellectual disability

We also note that it is difficult to grieve a death or a disability when there has been a long delay before the truth is known to family or significant others:

- When someone is "missing, believed killed" in armed conflict and hope stays alive that the report is false
- When someone is lost at sea, in the bush,[1] in the desert, in ice, or in any civil disaster when the outcome is not known for a long time
- When there is a series of deaths, as in the early days of the HIV-AIDS epidemic, in wartime, or in any situation in which one death follows another and either the survivors are unable to grieve continuously, as in a long-term epidemic, or they are too "busy" (because of the circumstances) to be able to set time aside for grief over those who have died. In any such situation, the need to deny one's grief is an adaptive defense for the time being, but it can then be difficult—sometimes impossible—to resolve grief that has been on hold for a long time

What Does *Change* Mean?

Change means different things in different situations. For some, it means that life with a permanent illness or disability becomes bearable instead of intolerable and suicide is no longer an issue. For others, change involves an alteration in attitudes, a lessening of guilt, or an expression or resolution of anger so that relationships are easier and more fruitful. Some are able to change their difficult behavior so that life is simplified and less fraught with conflict or risks to health. Some have their sadness validated as they cope with loss and are strengthened to face with greater equanimity a painful or lonely future.

Why Is It Difficult to Cope with Loss?

I have come to see that grief itself is complex, that problems in coping with loss are even more complex, and that often all we can do is support the person, facilitate as much insight as the person can tolerate, and provide coping strategies through counseling, cognitive behavioral approaches, or whatever is deemed appropriate to the individual. No single approach to resolution is all-sufficient, and the music therapist who works in grief resolution needs a broad philosophical approach.

Only recently have I given a name to this philosophy, and perhaps it is only as one reviews a lifetime of work that one sees the whole picture. Whatever the reason, it is only since early 1998 (when I made a firm decision to retire from active hospital work and planned to write about my experiences) that I have come to an overwhelming recognition of the therapeutic significance of flexibility, of a wide basis of knowledge, and of a repertoire of clinical skills. It is this recognition that has led me now to describe this multifactorial way of working as Supportive Eclectic Music Therapy.

Eclectic can be a euphemism for inexpert dabbling—a dilettante approach based on simplistic levels of knowledge and scant expertise—but *eclectic* also has a genuine professional meaning (Gelder, Gath, Mayou, & Cowen, 1996, pp. 610–11). Brief eclectic psychotherapy is described as the approach in which the therapist strives to meet the needs of the individual client in a brief series of interventions by drawing on professional knowledge of a wide range of schools of therapy and by using genuine expertise that has been developed in a number of different approaches and methods. It is in this sense that the word *eclectic* is used in this book.

Supportive is used here with a double meaning. First, we consider the supportive nature of all music therapy, which provides comfort, resilience in facing the future, and a helpful milieu in which change may (or may not) take place. This approach is appropriate for those who are unable to benefit from the addition of intensive verbal interactions because of lifelong cognitive impairment, traumatic injury, or other brain injury, but need emotional support and validation (Bright, 1996, Bright & Signorelli, 1999).

Second, supportive music therapy is valuable when it is inappropriate to take the client too deeply into issues of transference, ego strengths and weakness, and similar matters, either because there is a risk that the client will become "stuck" in the illness mode or because the illness is so severe and so resistant to treatment that there is no prospect of change. In such situations, all we can do is facilitate the growth of the client's own defenses—and, where possible, those of society—to permit some measure of life-satisfaction and personal growth within the context of the illness.

Gelder et al. (1996, p. 609) describe such work thus: "Supportive psychotherapy is used to relieve distress or to help a person to persist despite difficulties, when all opportunities for problem-solving have been tried."

What Is the Recipe for Success?

To suggest practical ideas is risky because it can end up like a cookbook: "To make a successful outcome, take 1 patient, 1 music therapist, 1 keyboard, and 1 drum set; mix well together for 20 minutes and leave to cook at a moderate temperature until next week."

Or (risky, although some of the points are valid):

The 10-Step Menu for Successful Therapy

1. Disconnect the telephone.
2. Sit facing the patient, with the chairs one and one-half meters apart, but place your chair so that you are nearest the door in case you need to escape, also leaving an avenue of escape for the client.
3. Smile, making warm eye contact.
4. Say, "Hi! I'm your therapist for today and we shall be making music together for 30 minutes. I'd like you to choose from this list on the board the problem that is nearest to your own."
5. When client replies, respond by saying, "That's great. I am sure we shall learn a lot about each other today! Now tell me, what brought you to the hospital?" (Hoping the person does not reply "An Ambulance.")
6. Next move to the keyboard and play so-and-so, in the hope that it may have some relevance for the client's particular problem, but also because you know you play it rather well...
   and so on, ending with...

10. End by saying, "Good-bye. Have a nice day!"

But it is possible to be practical and give ideas that will work without giving a rigid list of instructions on how to do it. In fact the first steps in the questionable list above are both practical and sensible and grew not from theory but from practical experience of what "works."

- We must not accept phone calls during a session. If an urgent crisis arises, the ward secretary or nursing unit manager can knock on the door and tell us why we are needed or why the patient is needed. Interruption in this way is far less traumatic to the patient and to the general milieu of the session.
- It is sensible to sit so we can leave the room without the client being able to bar the way. I have only needed this precaution a few times, but if we do need to get out of the room for our own protection, it is vital that we have prepared the room for such an emergency. Equally important, we must not block the client's exit. (Discussed later, see "Assessment in Psychiatry" in chapter 1.)

The practical approach predominates in this handbook; there are references to the theoretical basis for the work, with citations for books and journal articles, but it is assumed that readers will already be familiar with general theories of grief and loss as well as psychiatric disorders and the consequence of various disorders in everyday life. It is also assumed readers will have undergone some personal development work in order to recognize their own areas of strength and vulnerability.

Which Approach Is Appropriate for a Given Situation?

We cannot decide in advance which approach will work for any given patient or client. As will be seen from the various vignettes, most sessions encompass a wide variety of techniques, and each component grows out of a recognized need. This may be disclosed in the client's words, body posture, and other behavior or through our own grasp of what has been going on in life for the patient and how the patient responds (and has responded in the past) to various situations.

The way a session proceeds is also determined by the nature of the problem. Working with a person suffering from dementia and with the immediate family (to help deal with both the patient's and the family's helplessness) requires a different approach from the way we work with a forensic client who, through medication, is coming to painful recognition that his or her reason for killing someone was a delusional belief born of schizophrenia.

Even in the first example given, working with the dementing individual requires a different approach from that needed by the family. The person with the illness needs support, the comfort provided by familiar music, and reassurance of still being a real person, in what is really a behavioral method. The family, on the other hand (depending upon the quality of preceding relationships), may need permission to be sad, disappointed, and angry at the effects on their own lives. When the illness is Alzheimer's disease of early onset, they may need to ventilate their fear of carrying a gene for the condition, and here we must know where they can find support and professional advice. Perhaps the relatives need permission to express relief that a difficult parent is at last unable to inflict further harm on family relationships, and so on. In ADC (the dementia complex associated with HIV-AIDS), the emotions associated with dementia are often extremely complex emotionally, particularly if the family feels or experiences stigmatization (Lippman, James, & Frierson, 1993).

The chapters that follow use case histories to illustrate various approaches and how these were chosen on the basis of the patient's needs and particular personality or style of thought and emotion. Many of the vignettes are from work in psychiatry with adults in middle or early life and from work with people grieving over other losses in middle or later life, but the approaches are useful in any age and with any situation involving people who need to express emotions through music and verbal interchange.

The supportive, eclectic approach can be used to help parents of disabled children, adult children of people with dementia, those who are disheartened after a stroke (or the significant others of such people), or those grieving about death or impending death. In fact, this approach can be used in any human situation involving painful change and complex adaptation.

How Many Sessions Should There Be?

As one reads through professional journals on psychotherapy, counseling, psychiatry, and allied topics from the 1980s to the present day, one is struck by the marked reduction in the duration of therapy as reported today. Has this change occurred only because of financial pressures of managed care or because of reductions of government funding, so that patients are discharged from the hospital sooner? Sometimes we are told this is an advantage because new mothers are better at home with their families, because hospital infections cannot always be prevented, because community care is better for those with psychiatric disorders, and so on.

It seems clear from general reading that psychotherapists who see people on an outpatient basis are under pressure to have shorter rather than longer series of sessions with their clients. They are expected to be able to demonstrate unequivocally the benefits accruing from their work.

It has been interesting to read and reread writings on "brief therapy" of the last thirty years:

- Michael Balint, well known for his book on the importance of the doctor's personality as a factor in treatment (1964), wrote about what he called focal psychotherapy, and although he did not emphasize a precise number of sessions, his approach was clearly intended to be short-term. Balint also spoke of focus and intensity of treatment to produce change and discussed the possibility of the family doctor (general practitioner, GP) achieving this in a brief interview in a busy family practice. Here "brief" was ten minutes (Balint, Ornstein, & Balint, 1982, p. 151).[2]

- David Malan (1976, p. 40), writing on *The Frontiers of Brief Psychotherapy*, set an upper limit of forty sessions for any treatment perceived as "brief" and recommended making this limit clear to the client from the very beginning.
- An article from the 1980s presented an historical survey of the current states of brief psychotherapy, giving figures that varied from three to forty, the average number being around twelve sessions (Rogawski, 1982).
- A 1996 article that described a series of therapeutic sessions in brief dynamic therapy suggested that up to twenty sessions would be classified as "brief" (Barber, Crits-Christoph, & Luborsky, 1996).
- With the newer developments of cognitive behavior therapy that are very different from the operant conditioning behaviorist approach of the Skinner era that was in common use by music therapists in the 1970s, we have seen the establishment of solution-focused brief therapy—concentrating on solutions to problems rather than their causes. Practitioners of this approach report that some improvements are seen in those who have had only a single session, and the average number of sessions for effective outcome was described in the book *A Handbook of Solution-Focused Therapy* as anything from a single session on, with an average of nine (De Jong & Hopwood, 1996, pp. 272–9).

When talking to a number of colleagues about our concepts of brief therapy, discussion as to what "brief" means today in music therapy elicited a variety of replies:

- One session a week for an admission lasting two to three weeks
- One session a month for four months
- One or two sessions a week for two weeks
- Daily sessions during a one-week admission

Thus "brief" may refer to a short admission, a small number of sessions, or both.

How does this affect music therapists? It may be that economic- and health-policy pressures prevent us from having long series of individual music therapy sessions and we have no option but to plan short-term therapy. There is, for example, no time today to allow the gradual working-through of transference and countertransference issues over a matter of months or perhaps years; we must find ways of dealing with such issues quickly but effectively. We must develop strategies for rapidly building the therapeutic alliance without which beneficial outcome is doubtful.

We are fortunate in that music—whether familiar from past experiences or improvised as expressing our difficult thoughts and emotions—seems to bypass some of that need for long-term growth of trust. Reflective improvisation[3] that validates those hidden feelings elicits quickly in the client a sense of being understood—and, being understood, a willingness to collaborate.

Annoying as it may seem that decisions about length of treatment are sometimes taken out of our hands, we can, without being Pollyannas, find that the outcome is better than we might have expected. It is important that we perceive brief music therapy not merely as long-term therapy squashed into a poor substitute for "the real thing," but as something to be developed positively, a process that is radically different from the long-term therapy once practiced by our forerunners in the profession. In doing this, we may discover that there are benefits in short-term work through distilling our interventions into a powerful essence that still has power to facilitate change in even our most difficult clients.

What Is the Correct Nomenclature?

The way one describes the people with whom one works is fraught with potential misunderstandings, whether they are seen in hospital, day-care center, or in consultations in the community. Some people perceive patient as indicating a destructive paternalism, preferring client or even consumer, and in this we need to conform to the approach of the facilities in which we work. (This is further discussed in chapter 11, in the context of writing up our work for international readership.)

Why Does Music Therapy in Grief Resolution Work?

There are several possible reasons for the effectiveness of music:

- Music reaches beyond words, and although the verbal counseling component of grief therapy is vital in bringing the changes into the realms of everyday life and relationships, it is the nonverbal nature of music that provides the catalyst for change.
- The unfamiliarity of improvised music can validate or assist disclosure of emotions; it can lead to projection, in which unrecognized feelings are "put onto" the music.
- Familiar music is highly evocative of memories, hidden or forgotten, and this can be so surprising to the person concerned that other memories also

come flooding into conscious recall. Music can bring to mind the days of infancy when apparently forgotten songs were sung at bedtime, to school days and the choir in which we sang (or in which we were not allowed to sing because we were "growlers"!). It can bring back days of happy courtship, disappointment and loss when a relationship ended or failed to fulfill its promise, and so on. (See also "Gatekeepers of Recall" under "Approaches in Grief Resolution with Individuals" in chapter 5.)

- Music gives access to the nondominant hemisphere of the brain, where much of our emotional processing appears to lie. This can be significant—and this is so (except for those unfortunate individuals who have required a commissurotomy[4] or hemispherectomy[5]) even though we are whole-brain people, maintaining communication from one hemisphere to the other, so that there is not a complete separation of the functions of the two halves of our brains.
- The rhythm of music is important in recall (Bartlett, 1932, 1995, p. 290), supporting detailed recollections of many kinds.
- For some, the physical sensation of vibration is significant, to find that one is moved by memories of past experiences as well as by those of the present—as when one walks into a great cathedral while the organ is playing and feels rather than hears the sensation of sound.

This book presents some ideas that have proved useful in supporting the integrity of the individual, not as a "patient," a "client," or a "consumer," but as a person.

Chapter 1

Referral and Assessment

Aims and learning objectives of this chapter:

- *Establish the purpose and methods of assessment that are appropriate to the individual client*
- *Expand knowledge of the conditions and behavior commonly found in the particular population served*
- *Develop interdisciplinary skills and relationships so that referrals are more informative and appropriate*
- *Become skilled in observations of behavior in clients*
- *Develop strategies for enhancing the value of assessment by building an alliance with clients*
- *Gain skills in drawing conclusions, but without these being "set in concrete," so that they may be changed as the work continues*
- *Develop skills in writing notes in the client's clinical file for effective information sharing with colleagues*

The Aims of Assessment

Although we depend in part upon referrals for bringing to us people who may benefit from music therapy, we also need an effective method of assessment to decide which people may benefit from our interventions and which approach should be used initially.

Preliminaries

Before we make a time for assessment, we must check on the client's use of language. Beware of the concept of "functional use of language." Many migrants and refugees acquire enough of the new language to be able to use supermarkets and follow traffic signs safely but are unable to discuss deep emotional issues, attitudes to grief and loss, or spiritual values. In this situation it is essential to work through an interpreter in at least the initial stages. Those who lose command of the new language when they are acutely ill sometimes regain it as their health improves. Migrants who have had a dominant hemisphere stroke or who have a dementing illness often lose their previous command of the learned language.

Before doing the assessment, we also need information about general health. Is there a major hearing or visual loss that might impede communication? Brain damage from a stroke, accident, or violence that will affect the client's communication, mental acuity, or emotional characteristics? Mental retardation or other syndrome that diminishes cognitive functioning or social functioning?

It is also useful to know how many sessions we may be able to have, assuming we decide that music therapy is appropriate for the client. In the past, and in some parts of the world even today, therapists see a client or patient for several months. The person can gradually gain insight into personal feelings through music therapy and work through issues of transference and countertransference. But in other places, we are limited to a brief period, and this alters the pace of our work as well as the choice of modality and style.

Aims in Assessment

The discoveries we hope to make in assessment can be listed as follows:

- **Personality:** Is the client open in discussions of difficult matters? an emotionally "locked-up" person? suspicious, perhaps paranoid? frightened? hopeful? capable of deep insight? a "concrete" thinker or capable of abstraction?
- **Cultural background:** Does the client think "psychologically" or with a simple education and outlook?
- **Musical preference and experience:** What musical approach or genre will evoke a positive and trusting response?
- **Spiritual standpoint:** Is the client agnostic, atheistic, New Age, Christian, Jewish, Muslim, Buddhist, animistic? This has important implications for life, disability and illness, dying and death.
- **An overall impression:** Can this person work toward change or, in situations where change is impossible, accept appropriate support? What overall approach is likely to establish trust and an alliance between oneself and the individual?

Observations of all kinds, together with information from the referral or from colleagues, enable us to make our key decisions as to whether—and how—our work should proceed. The details that follow suggest how effective assessment can be incorporated into a working session.

Referrals

Referrals must be appropriate to our special area of therapy, and it helps if we give in-service talks to staff, to explain how we work and which patients or clients may benefit from our particular specialty. Because of staff changes, we need to give information at intervals so newcomers are educated.

Different units have different referral methods. In the early days at one hospital, I would arrive to find a note on the keyboard in my office saying, "Please see Mrs. _______. She loves music." I could only find out why Mrs. _______ needed help by asking the referring person, "What do you expect to be the outcome of my seeing this woman?" This proved more fruitful than asking, "What do you want me to do?"

After discussion, we decided to use the customary "Specialist Consultation Request" form, giving ample space for the person's history and the expectations of the referring person, which simplified the therapist's work. Hospitals or clinics where music therapy is well established will have their own referral system.

We may, after assessment, disagree with some of the opinions expressed in the referral, but it helps to know in advance it was thought music therapy would be useful. Sometimes the referral proves to be wrong. One referral said, "Please see Mrs. Bloggs. Her husband has just died. She is heartbroken and needs to ventilate her sadness." In fact she was coping badly with her "guilty" feelings of relief that an abusive relationship was over and she felt safe at last!

Some of the needed information will be in the referral, in the client's file, or available from colleagues:

1. How long has the person been ill or unhappy? Was the person previously hospitalized? When and how often? Have previous hospitalizations been at a particular time of year? If so, look for anniversary reactions.
2. What is the diagnosis, both provisional and differential?
3. What is the client's cognitive status? Usually a Mini-Mental score will be available for elderly clients, and we need to be familiar with the implications of this score. The Mini-Mental State Examination assessment tool, normally abbreviated in writing to MMSE and often called simply "the Mini-Mental," is widely used in the United States, and now in Australia (Folstein, Folstein, & McHugh, 1975). In the United Kingdom, the Abbreviated Mental Test Score, AMTS, is in common use (Hodkinson, 1972), but this is almost entirely a memory score, whereas the MMSE covers other aspects of cognitive function. Note, though, that the MMSE's criterion for the presence of impairment (24/30) below which impairment is likely, is known to have different implications when the tool is used with bright adults attending a memory clinic and when it is used with anyone disadvantaged by illness, psychosis, overmedication or illicit drugs, dysphasia, or dysarthria, or who is uncooperative (Pitt, 1994).

4. What effect has the illness had? For example, is the depressive illness so severe that there is suicidal ideation with plans, or is it limited to overall despair of the future, a wish to "wake up dead" as many people describe it? Ideally the referral will tell us of any major problems, as with the woman who was determined on suicide because of loss of control over her life following two above-knee amputations due to vascular disease. The referral for music therapy for grief resolution was a request to try to help her to acknowledge, understand, and express her fears and anger; if possible to resolve some of the issues associated with loss of control; and to support other treatment for her severe depression.

5. Is the person on medication, and if so, when was this started? Antidepressants and antipsychotic medications may take some time to work, and if medication has only recently been started or altered, we sometimes see gradual improvements that may or may not be the consequence of our own work.

   Long-term use of insulin will almost certainly tell us of lifetime diabetes (rather than the later-onset type), and adults have reported childhood memories of being "different," even stigmatized, by dietary restrictions due to diabetes, allergy, and other conditions. These memories further complicate emotional responses to their condition. We need to know about behavioral changes that indicate an incipient hypoglycemic coma so we can respond immediately and appropriately to the emergency.

   Older people with severe and long-established arthritis may in the past have been prescribed heavy doses of steroids and may have suffered bone-calcium depletion so that care must be taken with any movements. A patient in a geriatric rehabilitation unit was at risk of a broken neck, so severe was her decalcification, and although she wore a protective neck brace, I needed to take extreme care when moving her from room to room. I also needed to be aware of her grief and anger at the disability resulting from the treatment.

6. What is the financial situation for the patient? Is money available for an extended series of sessions? Will the patient be hospitalized long enough to plan for several sessions, or must we think of only one or two before discharge? Or is a short admission planned for therapeutic reasons?

Contraindications for Accepting a Referral

People who are extremely ill with paranoid delusions and other psychotic symptoms are often at first inaccessible to music therapy, and the intervention may be inappropriate because events and circumstances are taken into the delusional beliefs or the disordered thinking. This is especially true for improvised music, which may serve only to consolidate delusions rather than help to deal with them. If we ourselves and the music are thus included into the illness and the delusional beliefs, this can harm future possibilities. I have usually agreed with psychiatrists who have said, "I want this person to have music therapy, but I would prefer to wait until the worst of the florid symptoms have eased."

Writing on "dangerousness," Giles and Kraya tell us that the establishment of a close rapport may be dangerous because the therapist may become incorporated into the patient's delusions and so at risk of harm (Giles & Kraya, 1998). While it is improbable that we shall foresee such a situation arising when deciding initially whether or not to accept a referral, it is worth remembering the possibility of that risk if the patient's behavior is such that we are or may be incorporated into delusional beliefs as therapy continues.

It is rare today that any colleague sees music therapy as intrinsically harmful for a particular individual on the grounds that the person should not allow emotions to be dealt with. But there are times when someone is so vulnerable to decompensation that we are wise to provide only supportive rather than interpretive measures. This situation can arise in a psychiatric unit but can also occur in any health-care facility for those who are acutely ill, perhaps in the early stages following a stroke or spinal injury, when the future seems so fraught with tragedy that looking into the depths of one's emotions is temporarily inadvisable. Even if supportive music therapy seems unwise, the decision should be to *defer briefly* and not to *reject* music therapy. There are still opportunities in the future for dealing with painful emotions and looking into the future more positively.

None of the problems described above is sufficient in itself to preclude absolutely the use of music therapy for psychiatric clients, but discussion is needed. One needs to keep an open mind and come to one's own decision about the client's problems, and the reasons for these, with a plan of using music therapy for maximum benefit.

If we disagree with the referring professional, no matter how senior, we should be able to discuss our own views and—if our reasons are cogent and salient and our work is respected in the unit—we should expect to have our opinions taken seriously, even, on occasion, to the extent of a diagnosis being altered, as described in the vignette about David in chapter 10.

Observations of Grief in Relatives and Others

In our work we may have the opportunity to support relatives and friends of the client in their difficulties. We may be able to prevent depression or other illness, and their attitudes can affect the life, attitudes, and therapy of the client.

- We may sense a profound sadness, hopelessness, and powerlessness. In the face of severe substance abuse, physical disability, impending death, or chronic disabling psychiatric illness, fear, and despair are probably reality-based.

- Hopelessness, bewilderment, and despair for the future also arise as a normal type of response in an acquired disability of oneself or a relative, and this includes early dementia, where a significant proportion of sufferers are clinically depressed (Beats, 1996).
- Parents of children with severe behavioral disturbance can be so unhappy and anxious that they may appear psychiatrically disturbed when in fact their behavior has its origins in the lifetime problems they know lie ahead. The behavior of one such parent suggested that he planned to kill his child and then himself because the future seemed so hopeless, and the music therapist's "guess" on this proved accurate, fortunately in time for preventive action.

Making an Effective Assessment while Simultaneously Building a Therapeutic Alliance

Once it has been decided to do a music therapy assessment, we need to decide how to proceed. To sit across a desk with a person who is deeply unhappy or mentally disturbed, asking one question after another and writing down details on a card or ticking items off from a questionnaire, may seem efficient and effective but quickly imparts an atmosphere of apprehension and subservience. It also inhibits free disclosure because the person tends to sit silently, waiting for the next question.[1]

Equally, to begin immediately to play improvised music without any discussion at all is potentially bewildering, and even if we use precomposed music, we need to know about the person's life and experiences to know which music is loved and which hated. (But note that responses to hated music can be informative, once trust is established.)

The challenge is to use a combination of music and verbal exchange in order to find out a great deal of information in the minimum of time without scaring the person into incoherence or creating such a 'heavy' atmosphere that the person maintains a facade to hide a truth that is embarrassing or shameful.

Even in assessment we need to be aware of confidentiality and possible "splitting." If someone says, "I will tell you, but you must not tell anyone else," alarm bells ring for me and I wonder whether this is part of staff-splitting, whether I am to be told of suicide plans, or whether some other difficult situation is about to arise. My reply is always said with care so as to empathize as far as possible with the fear that may underlie the request for secrecy, and I will include these components:

> "You know that I am a part of the staff team here; we share any important information so that your treatment goes the right way for you because that

helps you to get better sooner. So I can't keep secrets because it is usually not helpful for you if one staff member knows something that others don't. But of course we don't *gossip;* any information sharing is always done very carefully, with only the person concerned."

Sometimes I add a comment of this kind:

"Your life may have been so difficult that it is hard to trust people, but I hope you will soon feel okay about dealing with even the very difficult things, as we work together."

The Assessment Protocol

The method I use, an informal approach, was derived from the work of Professor Tom Arie in the Department of Health Care of the Elderly in the University of Nottingham, United Kingdom. He found that elderly people were so frightened by formal assessment that they functioned far below their best, so he developed an informal conversational style that elicited all the key information but in the context of ordinary social chitchat.

I found that this response is not limited to older people. Those suffering from disabling grief, psychiatric disorder, or other emotional discomfort were similarly scared of questioning and guarded in their answers, so that a similar style to that used by Arie was appropriate for them too. Two sample assessments follow; although these are collations of some separate interviews, they genuinely represent the comments people have made and the way the ideas have been expressed and developed.

Assessment in Palliative Care

This is an assessment of Bernard, a 65-year-old man who has cancer and only a short time to live. Music therapy has been requested for him as a means to resolve some issues, for pain control, and to help his wife, Gwen, cope with her husband's death and the prospect of being a widow. English is his native language, and his former employment suggests that he is not academic in outlook but thinks in everyday terms about life and experiences. Thus a nonintellectual approach, both conversationally and in music, is indicated.

When I arrive in the early afternoon, Bernard is alone, sitting up in bed with the morning paper open at the racing page. He holds a pen and is marking off some items from these pages. This tells me that he has not lost all interest in life and that sporting events have been important in his life, and perhaps in his relationships, so that his social circle may have been focused on the racetrack, and his friendships with his drinking or betting friends. This may have affected his marital relationship, so it may need to be looked at in therapy.

Has his wife had her own circle of women friends? Has there been a close partnership between them? It has been said that one cannot counsel people about death unless one knows what pattern their relationship has followed—doing everything together or the husband having men friends and doing "his thing" and the wife still attached to her family, "doing her thing" (Ellard, 1968).

In this précis of an extended interaction, MT = Music Therapist, B = Bernard, and G = his wife, Gwen.

I put the electric keyboard on the floor where it is not very obvious, yet not hidden.

MT: Hello, Mr. ______, I am the music therapist, and your doctor suggested that we spend some time together. I know you are having quite a lot of pain, and it's a really difficult time for you altogether. Sometimes music can help.

B: *Music?* I don't think that can help me *now.* My music days are over.

MT: Yes, it probably does sound a bit trivial with all that has happened lately. *(Pause)* Was there any kind of music you liked in the past?

B: "I hated music at school. I couldn't sing in tune, and they made me pretend to sing in the choir, opening and shutting my mouth like a puppet. I felt a right Charlie, I can tell you, and the other kids used to groan whenever it was time for singing lessons and I turned up. But I did like playing the drums in the school band. *(Brightens up)* They said I had a good sense of rhythm, even if I was a groaner in the choir! We used to play for parades and around the racetrack when the local Show or the Picnic Races[2] were on!

MT: That must have been great! I can imagine you leading the parade around that track with the drum hanging on a harness from your shoulders. What kind of music did you play?

B: "Colonel Bogey" was one, and "Waltzing Matilda." You could really march to them! And I used to make up my own words to some of the tunes to make the others laugh.

MT: I can imagine that! I see you've got the racing pages open. Were you involved in the racing business, apart from leading parades?

B: *(Brightens up somewhat)* Yeah, I've always followed the horses, wanted to be a jockey when I was a kid but I was a bit too heavy. *(He looks down at his emaciated body.)* Couldn't say that now, could you. *(This was said as a statement, not a question.)*

MT: It's hard, isn't it, when things go wrong and you feel... well... different. How long has it been since you first realized you were really unwell?

B: *(Thinks)* I guess about two years since I went to the doctor. But Gwen had been at me for a while because I was getting those odd pains. But you know how it is—you don't want to think there's anything really wrong, hope for the best, I suppose.... Poor old Gwen, it's been tough on her, seeing her husband gradually disappearing, getting thinner and thinner—and crankier and crankier too.

MT: Yeah, pain and anxiety can make us behave differently and it's hard on those who love us. *(Pause)* Going back to the music, did you and Gwen ever share any songs together?

B: What, like "our song," you mean? *(I nod.)* Well we used to dance each Saturday night at the Church social, we were real good. And there was one song… *(Tears fill his eyes, he turns away in the hope I won't see them, but he cannot speak.)*

Pause. I hand him the tissue box without comment, except for gentle "Mm… it's okay to feel sad, you know," *in an accepting tone of voice.*

A few moments later, when he has regained his composure:

MT: Look, is Gwen coming in to see you today? I could probably play it for both of you. *(B nods and says indistinctly, "Three o'clock.")* But before that, could we also look at whether music would help you to deal with your pain? Maybe it sounds a bit odd, but tension sometimes makes pain worse, and music seems to help us relax. *(Pause)* Did your mother ever sing to you to help you go to sleep?

B: She sang something so funny that you'd never think of it as a lullaby, but it used to make me feel happy, and then I'd go to sleep!

MT: What on earth was it? Do tell me!

B: Well, she was a Scot and she used to sing "I belong to Glasgow"—you know—about everything going round and round? Except that she sang it like roond and roond.

MT: Yes, I know. Look, I'll play it through a few times, gradually getting softer and slower. You close your eyes, think of your mother, and see whether it helps you feel a bit sleepy, even if you don't actually go to sleep. But I promise I'll come back later, in time to play for you and Gwen.

I pick up the keyboard and put it on the bedside table. I play the requested song, first mezzo forte, then with diminishing volume, and more slowly with each repetition. B smiles, then his face relaxes and he turns on his side, his breathing changes to suggest he is asleep. As I move quietly away, I realize that—because of B's tears—I forgot to ask the name of the song. I hope that my repertoire will include the item, it is probably from around late 1930s to 1940s when the couple would have been in early adult life.

Later, 3 P.M.

As I enter the room, I see that G is sitting next to the bed, looking thoughtful. There is no great conversation going on, no eye contact. I move to the bedside and introduce myself.

G: *(Flat tone of voice)* Yes, Bernard told me you'd be coming.

MT: *(Sits down and is quiet for a few moments)* I know you've been having a difficult time for a couple of years. It's so difficult just to watch someone being ill, isn't it? We feel sort of powerless. Bernard said that you had to persuade him to go to the doctor. He said that must have been hard for you. *(G turns abruptly to look at her husband, and he looks somewhat ashamed as he nods.)* He also told me you used to have a special song you danced to, when you were first getting to know each other, and I wondered whether you'd like to listen to it together? When someone has been in hospital for a long time, there are so few "normal" things you can share. It's all treatment, doctors, tests, waiting, and worrying isn't it. Can you tell me what the song was?"

G: It was that one about "Always." Okay, you can play it if you want to, I suppose.

I begin to play the waltz, using a set waltz rhythm accompaniment at a moderately slow pace on the electric keyboard and a clarinet tone for the melody. B and G turn to look at each other, their eyes meet, B stretches out his hand to G, and she takes it. They move their hands together gently as the music continues, and both begin to cry.

MT: It is okay, you know, to share all kinds of feelings. But you need me out of the way for that. I'll look in tomorrow, around the same time. *(G and B both look briefly across with half-smiles and nod, before going back to look at each other. Quiet conversation is beginning.)*

What Did This Assessment Show?

- Bernard's comments about his weight loss, although presented in a semi-jocular manner, probably indicated deep feelings about changes caused by cancer.
- His comments also showed that he had delayed going to the doctor. Did Gwen feel resentment, in believing that an earlier consultation could have led to successful treatment of his condition? Her sudden look at Bernard and his shamefaced nod support this supposition, as also does her flat voice about the song, but this may simply be a part of her general sadness.
- Bernard's preference in music makes it necessary to use familiar or popular music initially, although later it may be possible to use improvisation and songwriting (he commented about making up his own words, although these were obviously only humorous![3]).
- His ability to sleep while his childhood lullaby was played indicates a capacity for relaxation. This must be charted and discussed with the staff member involved in decisions on pain medication.
- The fact that he and Gwen had danced together to a special song suggested using that music to try to recreate a lost relationship—always put under strain by long hospital treatment and fear of death, whether or not the relationship was good to start with.
- Planning: I must also check on general views on life expectation. The referral said "a few weeks," but what was meant by this? I'll check how often Gwen can be present and whether it's always in the afternoon. I could work with Bernard alone in the morning and see them together in the afternoon. I'll ask other staff members about Gwen.

This assessment could not tell every detail of what is going on. It gave no indication of whether Bernard had been a heavy drinker or what areas of conflict there were, other than his initial refusal to seek medical help. Perhaps his strong interest in racing led him to spend too much money on betting and, if so, does this need dealing with or can it be left? Nor could the assessment lead to definite plans being made, but it provided a picture of the man himself with some idea of what the relationship had been like, and the whole interview constituted both a start to therapy and an assessment as to what might be achieved. Although it is seldom possible to resolve each and every problem in the short time before death, a general rapprochement leads to general forgiveness without every detail being listed and remitted. Plans for the future might include some of the spiritual aspects of facing death; even those who appear very tough or down-to-earth in their outlook frequently need to have this side of life dealt with, to whatever extent is appropriate for them.

Assessment in Psychiatry

There are additional matters for observation in psychiatry, when it seems that the patient

- is listening to inner hallucinatory voices or watching hallucinatory images;
- shows hyperacuity and hypervigilance;
- is talking in a way that indicates delusional ideas and fantasies.

We take special note of disordered thinking, especially what is called "derailment" or "knight's move" thinking (the latter named for the moves made by the knight in the game of chess[4]). This is associated with thought disorder, as also is interruption of the train of thought by intrusive thoughts (Gelder, Gath, Mayou, & Cowen, 1996, p. 8).[5]

The following sample assessment illustrates ways of gleaning information by careful listening, interaction, and observation during a session that combines assessment and intervention. In this sample, MT = Music Therapist and J = Jim.

The Referral

"Jim is forty-two years old, unmarried, no immediate family, query suicidal but so far no disclosure on this. He describes poor parenting as a child; left school at sixteen to work in a factory. Crisis team says that neighbors report Jim always rather a loner. His girlfriend walked out two weeks ago; Jim needs music therapy for grief resolution. Has been drinking heavily for several weeks but is not, as far as is known, a longtime abuser of alcohol. No illicit drug use is known. Possibility of suicide was justification for admission. No history of violence, but could arise.

"Please assess this patient for music therapy for grief resolution with a view toward undertaking treatment. Admission of probably only two to three weeks. Unlikely that he would be available for outpatient follow-up sessions."

Reading Jim's file gives me further information. I find that he was brought in by the community crisis team on Tuesday (today is Thursday) after neighbors rang to express concern that they had not seen Jim for three days but were sure he was in the house. They normally saw him each day setting off to buy a paper or get milk or to put out the garbage bin on Monday nights, but he had done none of those even though garbage day was past.

The provisional diagnosis made at the time of admission is depression (not psychotic), query suicidal ideation. From this I knew that his belt would have been taken from him at admission and that, as a precaution, there were no hooks on any doors or cupboards in the unit.

The differential diagnosis noted on the admission form is adjustment disorder.

Antidepressant **medication** (specified) was prescribed by the registrar who admitted him (but I know that this medication will not yet have had time to take effect).

The treatment plan is for an admission of not more than two weeks because of risk of dependency; the patient needs to deal with past losses and build self-confidence. A case manager (from Community Mental Health Team) is to be appointed before discharge. I see that there has been a referral to the clinical psychologist, but that he has not yet seen Jim. I plan to speak to the psychologist at lunchtime Journal Club.[6]

The social worker's notes express concern about Jim's lack of job skills, probable need for cheaper accommodation now that his girlfriend is no longer sharing rent with him. The social worker has already put into motion the mechanics of getting Jim's name onto a public housing request list and has started mechanism for sickness benefits, "Perhaps obtain a disability pension depending on how treatment goes?" "Jim likes team sports. Could this be useful?"

Later that morning:

MT: Hello, you must be Jim Brown. Do come in. That chair over there is probably the best; then you won't have the light from the window right in your face." *(J sits down, does not move chair before doing so, and is thus in a position about 2 meters away, at an angle of about 45 degrees, thus avoiding overconfrontational eye contact but permitting ready eye contact if this proves comfortable.)*

Although I am close to the door, in case violence erupts and I need to leave quickly, his exit is not blocked. This is very important routinely, since a patient can become violent if he wishes to escape and the way is blocked by the therapist. We must prevent violence, not simply for our own safety but for the patient's benefit. Gabbard's comments on this are a must for all therapists working in psychiatry (1994, pp. 430–432).

MT: I'm Ruth Bright, the music therapist, and I work with people who are feeling unhappy and muddled about the way life has been going for them.

J: *(Sitting with head turned down so that I only see the top of his head, shoulders hunched, hands hanging between the knees, speaking after a pause in a flat voice)* Yes, Dr. Smith told me about you. He said you were very helpful, but I don't think anyone can help me. I just wish I was dead.

MT: It's pretty devastating to feel like that, isn't it, as if there is no point in going on. *(Pause)* Could you give me some idea of what life has been like for you? Have things gone wrong just recently?

J: I think I was never really wanted, and everything I do goes wrong. It's always my fault. I lost my job a year ago. Kylie's walked out on me. It's no good. I can't go on. *(Silence for a moment)* I'd be better off dead.

MT: People who say that sometimes mean that they actually have plans...

J: *(He sounds angry, triumphant)* I certainly *have*—a tube to go on the exhaust pipe of my old car. And as soon as I get out of here, I shall use it!

Comments

- Jim was described as depressed, and his posture, his initial flat speaking voice, and the content of conversation confirm this.
- Stronger tone regarding suicide plans is significant—symbolizes taking control. Also perhaps punishing someone by suicide? Look at this aspect later.
- Interesting that suicide plans disclosed so readily, probably the consequence of my making statement rather than direct questioning.
- Existence of plans confirms genuineness of wish for death, not, as for some, simply a feeling that they wish they could "wake up dead."
- Does plan to use car exhaust indicate that there is no risk while he is here or would he abscond to do it? Use another method if opportunity arose? Alert staff on this.
- No indication of psychosis or thought disorder so far, nor of hypervigilance. Not unduly guarded in responses.

MT: Was it Kylie's going that started you feeling hopeless *(very slight emphasis on the last word because it seems that life has always been difficult but perhaps not hopeless)* or was that the last straw?

J: Things have never been that good, and I'd been down ever since I lost my job this time last year, but Kylie going really pissed me off. I didn't know whether to be angry or miserable. Nothing was any use.

MT: Sometimes I meet people who have been ill and hospitalized quite often for a long time, but perhaps this is the first time you've had some help and talked to anyone about your feelings?

J: Yeah. It was only when the neighbors got worried about me and those people brought me to hospital.

MT: *(Speaking gently)* Jim, it does sound as if you feel that you've reached the bottom of the barrel at the moment. *(He nods. I pause.)* It may seem a bit odd to talk about music when you're deep in your feelings of disappointment and so on, but sometimes it is really useful for expressing our feelings. I wonder what music has meant to you in your life? Is it something that brings your feelings to the surface or helps you express them?

J: I used to want to play the guitar, but *(speaks angrily)* my parents never thought it was worth spending money on me for that. So all I had was *school stuff (sarcastically)*—pretty boring too.

This reinforces the ideas of Jim's perceived parental rejection. It also opens up the possibility of using music without much difficulty so long as it is does not remind him of school. But I must avoid uncontrolled catharsis because there is much hidden sadness and anger there, and this could well lead to a decompensation crisis if things got beyond Jim's feeling of control.

MT: You know, sometimes music can help people look deeply into life—and then start to find a way forward. *(Jim's head comes up at last and he makes eye contact with me with a slight look of interest.)* I'll start by improvising some music (that means I'm making it up specially for you) to describe how I think you may be feeling, and then we'll think which way we go after that. Close your eyes and decide what you think I am putting into music about the way life has been for you.

Improvisation follows that is basically diatonic but includes some atonal discords—treble clef C, middle C, and bass clef C played simultaneously, then changing middle C to C#, played all together in varying degrees of loudness, followed by moderately firm-toned diatonic music, but with elements of sadness, confusion, and uncertainty. These last feelings being symbolized by unfinished cadences, unresolved discords, sudden changes in dynamics, and tempos that interrupt when things seemed "settled."

The music draws to a close after about two or three minutes, ending slowly and with two open fifths played together to end, on middle C with the G above, and the G and C below this in the bass clef; these notes are chosen because they are ambiguous tonally, as in the opening of Beethoven's Symphony no. 9, where one is uncertain, when first hearing the work, whether this is to be major or minor in feeling.

A few moments of silence. Jim opens his eyes, his face bearing an expression such as one imagines on a traveler who had returned from outer space. Eye contact is maintained from here on, and he has changed posture to a normal upright position when sitting or standing.

MT: How was it for you?

J: (*Using the emphatic tone of voice often described as an "Aha!" response)* You really understand what it is to be me, don't you—the fear, the confusion, terrified as you wonder what will happen next, feeling useless....

MT: It's interesting that you mention fear because I don't think we had talked about that specifically. Can you tell me more about being afraid?

J: *(Strongly, his head jerks to face me even more directly. He speaks with escalating anger)* Fear? Who *wouldn't* be afraid when nobody cares? You can't get a job, people reject you, you feel helpless! I manage to hide it so people think I'm okay, but underneath I am scared shitless. But I'll show 'em *I am* in command!

MT: How?

J: You know—that tube I told you about—killing myself!

MT: *(Speaking strongly)* Jim, does it *have* to be death? Is there any other way you could be in command, but decide to keep going?

Jim shrugs his shoulders but does not react angrily to the thought that he might be able to bear to go on living. As I continue speaking, I am drawing sketches of four faces on the whiteboard (see sketches in chapter 3), showing happiness, sadness, anger, and terror (the last is similar to a simplification of Munch's work "The Scream").

MT: It sounds as if you maybe have a mask you wear for the world to see, but underneath it's different. Which one of these is the mask, and which are underneath?

J: The mask is this *(points to the smile)* and the others are underneath *(pointing to all the other three with a sweeping gesture).*

I improvise music for each face in turn, about 45 seconds each: cheerful carousel-type[7] *music for the first in G major, a melody in D minor with chords in the bass for the second, a loud discordant chord sequence for the third, and for the last, a tentative series of notes without rhythm or tonality, edging about the keyboard in half steps and some whole steps or leaps of fourths and fifths, played softly but with occasional crescendos and loud chords.*

J: That's about it, Ruth! *(The first time he has used my name, and the tone of voice suggests trust. Pause.)*

MT: You know, when you talk about your life, it sounds as if you have always had a burden. *(As I speak, I am drawing a stick figure with a heavy sack on its back making the posture stoop forward.)* What has been in that sack for you?

Jim stands up without being asked and takes the board marker from me, to write in Rejection, fear, anger, hopeless.

MT: Which is the worst?

J: Fear... and it's part of the anger, I think, because you're always afraid someone will reject you if they know you're raging inside. But perhaps they guess? Do you think *that's* why...

MT: Why things go wrong?

J: Yes, is that why people don't want me?

MT: That's something you may like to think about. But sometimes people are scared as well as angry, scared of what is next... because life has been too hard.

J: *(Thoughtfully)* Mmm.

Silence.

Comments

- This last section has revealed many useful concepts and, probably, confirms suspicions that Jim's plans for suicide are part of his anger over rejection.
- His responses also reveal a capacity for insight, suggesting that his heavy drinking is only recent. Otherwise he would probably have frontal-lobe damage and only be able to think concretely.

MT: Can we work together on this for a bit, see if we can put any of this into music together? You take the top of the keyboard, and I'll take the bottom and we'll see how we go.

J: But I've never played the piano—it'll be *awful! (He laughs slightly at this!)*

MT: It'll be okay if you just use the black notes. You'll be surprised I think!

We move chairs so Jim has command above middle C and I am below him.

MT: Let's work first on those three faces—let's do the happy one first, then change.

I improvise music initially to represent good cheer, then change to suggest sadness and confusion. Jim's playing is haphazard, fingers jumping from note to note without plan or pattern, but he keeps going. Then I start to provide only slow supporting chords while Jim's playing begins to have a sense of purpose, moving slowly across the black notes, first with the index finger of his right hand and then using both hands with one finger each and the movement becomes more coherent, with a modal feeling about it, the D# predominating as a quasi-keynote. As we play, I introduce stronger chords with some internal dissonance and a slight increase in speed, and Jim's playing becomes agitated, faster and louder, as the fingers join in clumps, almost fists, and discords follow rapidly after each other.

At this point one must make a therapeutic decision—this is giving Jim the chance to express his feelings, as was intended, but is it useful catharsis or is it frightening Jim, with the risk of a psychotic crisis if we persist? I decide that the catharsis has gone far enough for the time being and that Jim needs help in containing his own anger, so I change to play more slowly, with firm holding chords in the major, using white notes as well as black, and playing at a somewhat greater volume than Jim. Gradually Jim's playing calms down and there is a feeling that he has taken control once more. We end with a mood of quietness and confidence, not related to any one of the sketched faces.

MT: How was that for you?

J: A bit scary in patches. I thought it was all going to be too much for me and my anger was going to take over completely, but we seemed to end up quite positively, didn't we! *(Does the "we" show that an alliance is starting to develop?)* Somehow the music at the bottom [of the keyboard] helped me calm down and take control.

MT: The sort of control we talked about with those faces, where you just hide things?

J: *No!* Something a bit more positive than that!... as if I was being myself in control and not just pretending to be on top of things. *(Able to disagree with the therapist—a healthy step forward.)*

MT: *(After a few moments for reflection)* Generally I draw a set of ten steps on the board and ask people where they are at the moment. Hold on a minute and I'll draw them for you now. *(I draw ten steps. At the top the sun is shining, a tree casts a shade for a person sitting underneath with a basket nearby. An arrow points off to the side of the picture.)* That's you sitting under the tree. You've got a picnic basket beside you. I'm not sure what's is in it, but I hope it's not alcohol! *(Jim laughs, no denial of the implication that alcohol was a possibility.)* You are sitting down because it is has been hard work for you, helping yourself to get better. But you're not going to stay there. You will move on. *(I point to the steps again.)* If the bottom step is where you'd be if you felt despairing, and the top is you when you're feeling okay about yourself, where would you put yourself right now?

Which step are you on today?

Wording is carefully chosen—"hard work helping yourself to get better"—reinforces the sense of alliance, the shared responsibility in the tasks of healing. Jim points to a position between steps 3 and 4. I hold the marker, ready to draw the stick figure with one foot on each, but stop to ask, Which way are you going—up or down?

J: *(In tone of surprise)* If you'd asked me at the beginning, I'd 've said down, but now I think actually that I might be going up! Maybe I... I *can* go on?

I put a flag into the figure's hand and ask Jim what I should write on it. He says, "I think I'll make it." *So I write this onto the picture, after deciding that it may be too soon to ask Jim to write it himself. He is not quite ready for that degree of commitment to life.*

As the session continues, we talk about this, his tolerance for the idea that he could go on living, perhaps a growing sense of hope, and I suggest that when we start to feel hopeful we can sometimes look back on things from the past in a different way. We touch on aspects of relationships with his parents, why he felt they did not want him. Their poverty may have been part of this; perhaps they truly could not afford music lessons and were not actually rejecting him through their refusal? He recalls a song his mother sang to him, "An Irish Lullaby." I play this and he sings a few notes of the refrain very softly; this reminds him that there were positive aspects of his mother's care for him.

Jim recalls his father being a drinker and being angry, sometimes beating Jim for no apparent reason, but he did take Jim to football matches and once came to see him run in the school sports carnival. Jim also recalls his father whistling as he worked in the garden, and fortunately I can play this remembered tune (also an Irish one, "Phil the Fluter's Ball"). I play it and Jim tries to whistle it—not very successfully, but enjoys the effort to do so.

Relationships with his girlfriend are too recently traumatic to be recalled with any wholeness, but he remembers a Beatles song they shared, which includes the words "I need somebody to love" and "I get by with a little help from my friends." He plays one of the bongo drums that are in the room while I play that song on the keyboard. I had not used drums earlier because of the risk that the anger potentially inherent in playing drums could lead to a crisis, but by this stage that risk appeared to be past.

He then acknowledges that his recent drinking made him a frightening person and made him impotent (he hopes this is only temporary). When he wasn't drunk, he was miserable over his loss of a job, so there was not much his girlfriend got out of the relationship, and it really did not live up to the ideas in that song. Loss of job was not due to drinking, he says, but to downsizing of the business.

The session has lasted forty-five minutes so I draw it to a close with a plan to meet next week, when I hope to include songwriting; he'll think about this and put ideas together, probably a song about hope, and we will work on it next week. I give him a copy on paper of the sketches from the board. He will also see the clinical psychologist, who is skilled in cognitive-behavioral techniques.

It has been recommended that clients be actively involved in the therapeutic process (Mackenzie, 1988). My custom fits this recommendation: asking clients to contribute to sketches on the board, to be involved in shared improvisation, and to do some preparation for the subsequent session—such as drawing a life road map or thinking of words for a poem or a song.

A Personal Theme

I ask whether he has any favorite music that suggests hope, for him to take from the session. He says he'd like to use the theme from the film *Chariots of Fire,* which made a strong impression on him when he saw it many years ago—he still recalls the tune clearly. We talk about the waves shown in the opening sequence of that film, the thought that waves can either bowl you over and break your neck or drown you, or you can use the strength of the waves to strengthen yourself, as the athletes were doing in the film.

As we say good-bye, Jim is cleaning the board, a symbolic way of saying that this was his session, not mine. I make a comment about staying alive until next week and say that this does *not* mean that he has my permission to kill himself when that session is over! Jim laughs and we part on a hopeful note. Afterward I realize that I had not checked to see whether the plans disclosed for killing himself were part of a plan to punish his girlfriend, but maybe this was not an important omission, and in any case my notes in the file will probably cause someone else to bring that up with him.

Comments for the File

- Jim presented as seriously depressed and socially isolated. This appears to be longer-standing than the time immediately before this admission; has he perhaps been dysthymic since childhood?
- He disclosed suicidal plans (by car exhaust) early in the session, with a strong component of anger as motivation. (Angry with girlfriend?) The risk appears to have abated but should not be ignored if he has a crisis, because another method may present itself in the unit or he may abscond to achieve suicide.
- Familiar music from relationships with parents and girlfriend used as basis for discussion. Jim was able to join in improvised music, expressing strong emotions, especially fear. Anger was also disclosed. But he was able to reassert emotional control. Jim no longer seems actively suicidal (although a crisis could rekindle this) and spoke of life ahead. He appears now to have good insight—which supports belief that alcohol abuse is of recent origin, as frontal-lobe function appears intact.

Plans for songwriting, further improvement, and discussion next week. *Chariots of Fire* theme chosen as representing battling against difficulty and succeeding. At the end of session, Jim seemed surprised and pleased at what was in the assessment with a phrase on the flag suggesting hope. Copies of sketches were given to Jim as memory aid.

What Did This Assessment Show?

- The diagnosis of depression at nonpsychotic level was confirmed. I suspect that the condition is not of such recent origin as it might appear, that Jim has suffered since childhood from dysthymia as described in the research criteria in DSM-IV, page 718 rather than on page 349 (American Psychiatric Association, *Diagnostic and Statistical Manual of Mental Disorders,* 1949).

- Jim's drinking is of recent origin only; there is no alcohol-related brain damage since insight and abstract thought are still intact.
- Relationships with parents: although far from perfect, difficulties may have been overemphasized through depression. Jim gained some insight on this. Some alteration was seen in the way he looked back on relationships with his parents.
- Did he inherit a vulnerability to alcoholism from his father, whom he reported as being a heavy drinker? If so, it may mean that alcohol is a more serious potential problem than might appear. (It seems probable that vulnerability to alcoholism can be inherited; Vaillant, 1983, p. 311.)
- Suicide plans were disclosed quite readily; underlying anger was the reason for these plans—anger with his girlfriend (see comment "I'll show them"), now-dead parents, and previous employer. Anger known to be a trigger for suicide. As written in the file, the fact that he planned to use car exhaust does not necessarily mean that there is no risk while he is in the unit. If he had a major crisis, the risk could rekindle and another method could be chosen or he could abscond.
- Jim is open to change within himself. This was demonstrated by alteration in mood through the session and the discussion that followed improvisation.
- Jim is willing to think in terms of the future, so plans can be made for components of music therapy that gently encourages future plans—but these must be realistic, as Jim has few job skills. Check with social worker if there is any progress on retraining programs.
- Jim has some gifts in music, mainly rhythmic, but he is willing to try new things. Although this emerged in the context of music (improvisation, playing bongo drums, planning to write a song about hope), it has important implications for Jim's future.

Assessment Tools Not Used in These Examples

Two projective techniques that were not used in the assessments described above can be useful in assessment as well as in subsequent sessions for ongoing evaluation of change.

1. **An artist's wooden (jointed) figure,** which can be bought at any store that sells art equipment. Choose one that is of reasonable size and that is strongly made because it may receive some rough treatment! Introduce the idea of reshaping a wooden figure by saying that it can be helpful to express one's own perception of mood in a visible way. Suggest that the client sets the figure in the posture to represent how he feels at this moment. Observe how the changes are effected, the client's facial expression while making the changes, and what posture is chosen: a protective and hunched fetal posture, a standing position with head hung down or with arms stretched

high in triumph, arms set as if ready for a fight, and so on. Check out whether your guesses about underlying emotions were correct by making statements rather than by asking probing questions. The concrete nature of this technique has proven useful for people with alexithymia,[8] and leads readily into nonverbal improvisation for many people.

2. A suitable **picture** on the wall of the consulting room or, if no appropriate artwork is present, a picture from one's stock of items on the shelf. It is useful to have a variety of pictures: city, town, village (including Norman Rockwell's *Saturday Evening Post* style), country, and seaside scenes, with and without people. I have found it important initially to use a picture *without* any human figures in order to get a feeling about the individual alone before assessing behavior in relationships.

   Point to the picture and ask, "Where would you want to be in that picture if you were there?" Then improvise music to express the feelings associated with the reply.

   The picture referred to below shows a country scene with a rough narrow track leading down to a small river, a group of large eucalyptus trees, a broken-down fence around a grassy area with sheep dotted randomly around the foreground, a hill in the distance, and a sky that is a mixture of clouds and clear blue.

   Some responses to that picture have been powerful, as with Jack, who, in the first session, said in a bitter tone of voice, "I'd be hanging from the branch of that tree." This was helpful because it confirmed the guess that the motorcycle accident in which Jack had almost been killed some weeks before he became severely depressed had actually been (as suspected by staff although denied by the patient) a suicide attempt. He also related strongly, in the second session, to the playing and singing of Schubert's song "The Trout" (suggested because he had been a keen fisherman) and, in my subsequent discussion with his psychiatrist, we both suggested that the sympathy shown in the song for the helpless trout matched Jack's own feelings of helplessness and powerlessness in dealing with his life circumstances, his ambivalence about his sexuality, and the quasi-paranoid feelings he had of being the victim of a sportive fate.

   After an extended admission, Jack looked again at the picture during his final session and said cheerfully, "I'd be out on a horse rounding up those stupid sheep!" Interestingly, he had no recollection of his previous suicidal ideation.

   Others have said of this same picture, "I'd be behind that tree, where I'd be safe." "I'd be on the top of the hill watching what was going on in the valley, but nobody could see me." One man, on the eve of discharge after an admission for attempted suicide, said, "I'd want to fix that fence so it was some use."

One picture that was painted for me to use in this work depicted a curved sunlit beach with low waves breaking on the sand, a tall branching tree, and some low bushes in the shadows behind the beach with a headland at the end of the bay. I have also used a 24″ x 15″ photograph of the North Australian Tropical Rain Forest, with almost no sunlight showing and enormous tree ferns and tangled lawyer vines.[9] Some clients have found this photograph frightening but others have found the darkness and solitude to be reassuring.

Such pictures are not as revealing as the more structured Thematic Apperception Tests (devised by Morgan and Murray in 1935 and later discussed by Stein [Gieser & Stein, 1999]) but, overall, are informative to the therapist. They are often helpful to the client also, in helping to crystallize previously unacknowledged fears, thoughts, and feelings and lead into their expression through music.

Treatment Plans

Assessment leads into decision making about music therapy interventions. Questions we ask ourselves are, for example:

- Is there a way in which music therapy can help?
- Should the aim be an extended series of sessions or brief therapy only? (The answer may be decided for us by other staff's decisions about the length of the admission or by the managed-care office as to how many sessions will be covered financially.)
- What approach will be best suited to this person's needs and his own orientation?
- On the basis of the previous decision, who is the best person to provide the necessary therapy and support?

Rejecting or Delaying Music Therapy

What factors emerging in assessment might lead us to refuse to accept the client or delay music therapy?

Accessibility was mentioned earlier, and it is improbable that we should be asked to assess an acutely psychotic patient. But, on rare occasions, delusional beliefs that make change impossible may be noted during music therapy assessment when they have not previously been discerned. In this case, we shall probably delay sessions until acute symptoms have eased.

Dangerousness is also something to be considered. I was asked to see a forensic patient whose father had died and who had attempted to kill his mother (and had injured her severely in the attempt) because he believed she had murdered his father. It was suggested that this young man would benefit from music therapy with me because, through processes of transference (I was much the same age as his mother), he could work through his angry delusional beliefs. I asked whether it would be possible to have a nurse present at our sessions, and on learning that it would not, I declined the referral until such time as his illness abated.

Antipathy to music, for whatever reason, requires thought as to whether to accept the referral on a provisional basis. My practice is to accept the referral conditionally if the client is willing to attend, and see what happens as we get to know each other.

The patient's capacity to benefit from therapy should be another deciding factor. Most music therapy today is short-term work, and in an article published in 1988 but still useful today, the writer discusses how we determine whether or not to offer brief therapy to any individual (Mackenzie, 1988). The criteria he listed as essential to successful outcome in brief therapy were

- a capacity to relate;
- psychological mindedness;
- motivation;
- demographic suitability (able to attend sessions, sufficient finances to be able to continue, and so on);
- adaptational strengths.

Summary

Comments from two colleagues are worth noting:

"People don't put their barriers up when it's music therapy."

"When I read the notes in the file about what has happened in music therapy, the patient suddenly jumps out of the page as a real person."

These are tributes, not to me as a person, but to the power of music therapy to support revelation and integration of the wholeness of the individual.

Chapter 2

Meaning in Music
The Basis for Grief-Resolution Work

Aims and learning objectives of this chapter:

- *Develop understanding of the emotional content of music and its different components, but also recognize the differences of meaning that may be assigned to or perceived in improvised music by individuals, depending upon culture, emotional state, or psychopathology*
- *Develop skills in improvisation in order to reflect accurately, in terms of a client's musical understanding, culture, emotional state, and psychopathology, the emotional content of the client's life history*
- *Develop skills to enhance disclosure and the establishment of the therapeutic alliance through improvisation and through the use of music that is familiar and meaningful to the client*

Meaning in Music

Universality or Cultural Diversity?

Music therapists are essentially involved with meaning in music. How much difference is there in the emotional content as perceived by the composer, the trained or the naive listener, and the academician? Do perceptions vary from day to day, even in the same individual depending on current emotional state? Do any two listeners hear identical emotional meaning in one composition or improvisation?[1] Does cognitive recognition of the meaning of a musical item as "peaceful" or "angry" lead to a change in one's mood to match that of the music? And can we, as therapists, discern with 100 percent accuracy the emotional content of someone else's improvisation? These are contentious questions, and all have implications for therapy.

Therapists argue about universality of meaning in music, but unless the terms are defined, the discussion is meaningless. Some people claim that music has a universal meaning, implying that each individual will "hear" the same emotions in a given piece of music and that emotions will be expressed in music consistently by all clients. Others (myself included) differ, believing that perception is affected by powerful cultural influences arising from the individual's ethnic background and from personal associations and experiences, with consequent learned behavior.

The passage of time also changes perceptions of meaning: English vocal church music of the twelfth century sounds strange to us today, perhaps unattractive, and (except for the enthusiast) the music rarely seems to match the emotion in the words.

Mendelssohn said that a word does not mean the same thing to one person as to another; only a tune says the same thing, awakens the same feeling. (Mendelssohn, 1842, quoted by Storr, 1992). Much as I love the music of Mendelssohn, I see his statement as being culturally influenced; he had (one assumes) never heard the variety of music now available to us—from remote villages in Indonesia, China, or the Philippines to the microtonal music of Indian tradition. Storr, the author who quoted Mendelssohn thus, goes on to say that Mendelssohn's statement can be true only for a given culture. Even the "children's chant" can vary in the notes and in the way it is used!

Universality is acceptable as a statement of *musical fact*—that D minor remains D minor for any musically educated listener, no matter what language he or she speaks. Yet even here there is confusion in that pitch has not remained the same through history and at some times there have been marked discrepancies even in one country. In Tudor England, for example, there was a difference of about five half-steps between domestic pitch (the lowest) and church music pitch (the highest), with secular vocal pitch in between, at about the same pitch as that we use today (Scholes, 1947).[2]

There is a popular stereotype that music written in a minor is "sad," but that music in a major key is "happy." But the emotional meaning of the music written in the key of D minor will depend not only upon the composer's intention but the listener's perceptions and may be influenced by the way the music is played; dynamics and speed of performance have powerful connotations for mood perception.

Definitions and Perceptions

We can discuss universality of meaning in music only when we decide what definition is given to the word *meaning.* Certainly the notes of C-E-G will always be heard (and described) by the educated musician as a major triad in the root position, and those with perfect pitch will identify it as being the triad of C major. This harmony, if preceded by the triad G-B-D (probably played with the addition of F# at the top) will usually be perceived as constituting a perfect cadence. This is *grammatical meaning,* universal to all who have studied the theory of music.

But if one believes that every individual throughout the world will hear this particular progression as having an identical *emotional meaning,* then the belief is questionable, untenable. Those educated in Western music may ascribe to the completion of the cadence a sense of comfort or finality. But it could also be perceived, by someone with a particular problem, as "blocking" by premature closure, preventing resolution of that problem rather than allowing further discussion. Failure to complete the progression, on the other hand, appears to represent for most Western-educated musicians a painful sense of incompleteness.[3] But would these same responses hold for a person from any place where Western music is still entirely unknown?

Factors that influence general perception:

- Cultural experiences in tonality, style, and instrumentation
- Age, social status, and educational background as related to everyday life
- Personal life experiences and associations with a particular item of music

Factors that influence perception in therapy:

- Projection[4] of material that has been repressed, due to psychopathology
- The dropping of defenses so that difficult material can be disclosed

Improvisation and Perception in Therapy

In therapy we observe

- projection of repressed inner needs, as an unconscious process;
- disclosure (often also referred to as "projection") of the needs that have been hidden or suppressed, the music having given permission for, and evoked, the disclosure;
- personal associations with known items, which may be congruent with the accepted emotional content of the music but which may strongly contradict that mood.

Our clients describe the emotional content of improvised (and therefore unfamiliar) music, but we may be uncertain as to whether this is projection or arises from personal associations. We also find that through improvised music different people express similar or identical emotions in very different ways. These differences of both perception and expressivity are frequently the key to insight (ours and the client's) and mark the beginning of change.[5]

Yet if we are to use improvised music in communication, often with those who find verbal discussion difficult, how can we proceed? Stige's discussion of the meaning of music is very helpful in this context, helping us to comprehend "the importance of seeing *meaning in music as local knowledge belonging to a specific language game*[6] *in a specific context.*" (1999, p. 64, emphasis added).

The implications are clear. Music that means one thing to a British therapist may have a radically different meaning to a client newly arrived from a primitive First Peoples background.

The thoughts that follow are therefore based on a belief that improvisation and its interpretation have a measure of universality within a given ethnic culture, but that there is no transcultural universality. The suggestions below are thus appropriate only for clients who share our Western musical background regarding tonality and style. We shall also find that perceptions of emotional content are influenced by a client's psychopathology; the paradoxical responses to and interpretations of our improvisation are among the most important and useful aspects of work in psychiatry.

We can prepare ourselves before starting the work by sitting at the keyboard at home, improvising music that we think portrays anger, sadness, despair, agitation, serenity, fun, journeying, striving, and so on, asking as many people as possible to listen and report back what they perceived as the emotional content of the music we played.

Research Results

My own research (Bright, 1976) demonstrated that, although there may be an overall understanding of the emotive content of music (which was unfamiliar and yet was composed in the style of one given culture), there will be significant individual differences, and it appeared that these tend to come from people with psychopathology.

Subsequent research used the same pieces as those composed for the 1976 study but interspersed these with unfamiliar music from widely different cultures, the emotional content of those items being already known to the researcher. The research investigated the responses of persons with Western cultural background to music of a familiar and of an unfamiliar culture; they were asked to select the emotional meaning of the music from a questionnaire, after listening to the composite tape recording. Subjects were drawn from a large population of people of diverse ages and levels of education.

Results revealed that it was impossible for untutored listeners from a Western culture to perceive the emotional content of music of different tonal and other structures, derived from cultures that were unfamiliar to them. Results were no more significant than in the null hypothesis (there was no more accurate perception of emotive content of each item of music from unfamiliar cultures than if the subjects had closed their eyes and stuck a pin into the list of descriptive words). But there was significant consistency in the interpretation of emotional content of items composed in the style of the familiar culture; untutored listeners tended to perceive feelings such as sadness, anxiety, anger, and happiness as pertaining to the same type of music (Bright, 1993).

Work in guided imagery in music demonstrates that, although certain musical structures in Western classical music elicit powerful imagery, the precise nature of that imagery will be influenced significantly by one's personal experiences and emotions (Erdonmez Grocke, 1999).

This must warn us of the dangers of interpreting the meaning of our patients' improvisations without also checking with them as to their perception of events. Although these comments are given here in the context of group improvisation, they are equally applicable to individual work. But it is easier in the latter situation to guard against therapist error.

We must, however, bear in mind that improvised music may bring material to the surface for everyone, whether a designated patient or our neighbor on the block, so that one or two paradoxical interpretations of our improvisation should not lead us to distrust our creativity and ability to express moods through music. But neither, if we are wise, should it lead us to start working out what is going on below the surface for our neighbor!

Practical Ideas

I have found that there are some features of music for which there are common perceptions of emotional content by people of Western cultural background. When used with the therapist's intuitive perception of the client's personal needs, our improvisation reflects back to our clients the emotions we believe to be hidden below the surface, but we also remember that the phenomena of projection and disclosure will illuminate the matter further. It is rare for an item of reflective improvisation to contain only a single feature; it is useful in most instances to incorporate several types of music into a single improvisation so that the listener can more readily perceive a personal life scenario, but one type may predominate if this seems appropriate.

- **Repeated chords of an open fifth, spread over two octaves and including notes in the bass clef, played with increasing volume from very low to very high:** when incorporated into an improvisation, these are usually perceived as symbolizing increasing tension or anger, but sometimes as escalating anxiety or fear.
- **Sequences of major chords, whether played as close triads or extended chords:** these usually give a sense of solidarity, perhaps safety—although, depending upon the person's outlook and personality, some will interpret these as boring and unadventurous.
- **A tonal melody, played with increasing pitch as it moves up:** this often brings feelings of hope and optimism. **A melody with a definite climax**

point, ending with a downward 'home move' cadence may be perceived as more complete, although much will depend upon the chords used to harmonize the melody.

- **Sudden jerky changes of tempo, meter, or key:** these are useful to suggest uncertainty, conflict, the feeling of "I wonder what will happen (to me) next?" The style of modulation affects the emotive content profoundly, whether we move smoothly or by "crash" modulations. These help to convey one's own understanding of the client's uncertainties in life or in the present treatment.
- **Diminuendo combined with ritardando:** this is sometimes perceived as a comfortable way to finish, but it has also been perceived as indicating life and certainty disappearing in a frightening manner, depending upon the harmonies used at the end.
- **A descending series of notes can be harmonized in an atonal manner (or if preferred, with predominantly minor chords) and played more and more slowly and with a loss of volume as the tones descend. A minor scale can be used, but whole steps are often more effective because they lack the sense of completion such as is perceived in a known musical scale:** this pattern is usually perceived as symbolizing loss, discouragement, growing sadness, and perhaps despair.
- **Music that includes repeated seconds and/or sevenths, whether with a half step or a whole step between them, and played as a series or repeated on the same note:** this is usually heard as symbolizing conflict, anger, or uncertainty.[7]
- **Playing the notes as the open minor seventh, with greater spacing by additional octaves:** this appears to reduce the sense of tension somewhat, and the interpretation may differ, but usually there is some perception of imperfection or tension, although less than that deduced from the major seventh.
- **Changes of tonality:** these have different effects on the listener depending on whether there is smooth modulation or an abrupt change to a distant key (C major to A minor produces little sense of conflict, but C major to G# minor without a bridging passage gives a feeling of shock or surprise).
- **The way any music is played, its speed and dynamics, profoundly affects the perception of mood.** An unfamiliar piece played slowly and softly can mean one thing to the listener but the same item played loudly and rapidly will probably be interpreted quite differently.
- **The 6/8 rhythm, of 6 eighth notes (quavers) to the measure (bar) and played slowly at around 60 beats to the minute:** this is usually heard as gently rocking and soothing, but **when played at 120 beats to the minute** is heard as cheerful and full of bounce.

- **Four quarter notes (crotchets) to the measure (bar) played at around 70 beats per minute** have a martial ring, but, **played more slowly,** music with this meter may be heard quite differently, depending on other qualities of the music and the inner attitudes of the person. It may describe determination, power, solidarity, or doom.
- **Improvised music that contains slow lower mordents 8 (using the whole step below the main note) or passing notes that do not resolve or do so very slowly** are often heard as symbolizing yearning, disappointment, or sadness, and described verbally as meaning "If only...." To play with decreasing speed and volume the first five notes of the A minor scale with a single A holding an octave lower in the bass, with an inverted mordant on that last note that is then held, is almost always heard as sadness, regret, or similar emotional quality. Thus: A—B—C—D—E/G/E

Explanations to the Client

When we introduce the playing of improvised music to reflect the emotions congruent with the life story we have heard, we should *not* state which emotions will be shown, lest that locks the client into those feelings and excludes others. Instead we should say something to this effect:

"It sounds as if your life has been difficult and complex. I'd like to improvise some music to express a little of what you have experienced. Close your eyes and listen and see what thoughts come to your mind as I play. The music will be unfamiliar, and some of it may sound quite strange. We can talk about that later."

We play intuitively. Confirmation is there when—as we finish—the client weeps, makes eye contact, lets out a sigh of relief and says, in effect, "You really know what my life's been like, don't you?" or tells us that the music has brought to the surface an emotion that has not previously been disclosed verbally.

It is important to note that the mood evoked in the listener does not necessarily match the mood of the improvisation. The person who has kept anger under control may well become more peaceful upon hearing it expressed reflectively; on the other hand, the person whose anger has not been recognized by the therapist and who hears peaceful music played, purporting to be reflective, may well become extremely angry!

Insight during Improvisation

Exactly how improvisation is presented and how the work proceeds, whether it is fruitful or merely time-filling, will depend upon the health of the person—physical capabilities, emotional behavior, and psychological mindedness—and the skills of the therapist in gauging mood, readiness for exploration, and other factors. We also need the capacity to recognize when the session is becoming too heavy for the client to cope with and the skills to effect a change of mood without this being jarring to the particular client. This too is concerned with meaning in music.

When there is shared improvisation, we may be able to sense what the meaning of the music is for the client, but we need to verify this, directly or indirectly. This process has the added advantage that it can lead to further disclosures and support songwriting and other work.

Personal Comments

There are those will disagree profoundly with what I have written, whose philosophy is based upon universality rather than cultural diversity, believing that the same sound has the same meaning for every individual, well or sick, educated in an English public school and university or growing up in a remote village in central Africa.

But my opinions are based on observation of people from a wide range of educational, social, racial, and ethnic backgrounds and are supported by research. I firmly believe that, as therapists, we must come without preconceived ideas as to what music will mean to our clients and we must be willing to learn from them, and willing, if necessary, to change.

Chapter 3

Methods, Techniques, and Protocols in Music Therapy for Grief

Throughout the book I assume that experienced therapists will have already gained basic skills in counseling and/or psychotherapy. This book is, therefore, not a counseling textbook but a practical handbook of applications of particular methods and techniques in an integrated, eclectic music therapy approach.

Note that none of the protocols, methods, or techniques described in this book are restricted or controlled by the author. It is hoped that acknowledgment will be given for the source of the ideas. They are presented here for music therapists to use creatively, develop, and take further.

No ideas, no techniques, however many years they have been in the making, are complete and perfect. New applications are always being found by those who have empathy and imagination, and who are committed to facilitating change in those whose lives are out of control.

Aims and learning objectives of this chapter:

- *Become more adept at deciding which approach or approaches to use with any given individual*
- *Develop an overall eclectic approach in grief resolution, extending knowledge and understanding of a range of methods and techniques*
- *Become familiar with the use of reflective improvised music in order to enhance support, disclosure, and insight for clients whose problems have been difficult to treat or who have not previously received help*
- *Facilitate, if possible, the resolution of matters that are disclosed*
- *Develop the use of shared improvisation and songwriting aimed toward resolving previously blocked grief through insight and expressivity, and providing support for those whose problems are not amenable to change*
- *Gain skills in the use of graphic techniques to provide support and enhance insight and the processes of change*

- *Gain preliminary insight into the use of the empty-chair method and other symbolic processes of communication that may lead to grief resolution*
- *Develop skills in selecting a personal theme for clients to take into the future*
- *Enhance counseling skills in an eclectic, integrative approach to the many aspects of grief and loss that are encountered in hospitals, clinics, and the community*

After Assessment

When assessment is complete, we have to decide whether group work, individual work, or a combination of the two is most appropriate for the client; which school of music therapy will be most useful to the client's health; and whether a single approach is indicated or a combination of several in an eclectic approach. For some clients, the initial decision was made during assessment, and therapy (including the beginning of the sense of alliance) has already started. But for some clients, interdisciplinary discussion is required after assessment.

The decision about group or individual work is not either/or; it can often be both. Individual work provides privacy for dealing with difficult topics or those that are seen as shameful or guilt-laden, but the group provides opportunities for sharing an activity, for cooperation, and for care and consideration toward each other.

Neither does the choice of approach necessarily depend upon the diagnosis. The direction of our work will vary with the individual, and most of the suggestions presented here are appropriate to use—with adaptation to personal needs—for any disorder. And in any case, disorders cannot always be neatly sorted into categories; someone with a phobia or an eating disorder, for instance, may well have unresolved issues associated with childhood abuse, without those having been perceived initially as the primary problem (Bryer, Nelson, Miller, & Krol, 1987).

Therapy in the Group

For grief resolution, the group milieu is helpful in supportive work, for example in a cancer or AIDS support group when the philosophy is that of *living with* the disorder rather than *dying from* it. People with a doubtful, disheartening prognosis rarely wish to spend every minute of the day and night thinking about the outcome of their illness but need to spend some time in happy activity either alone or with others, not as denial of the possibilities of bad outcome, but to set these possibilities aside for a time in order to focus on positive aspects of life and relationships. Music group work is ideal for this, whether it is songwriting, group improvisation on tuned and untuned percussion instruments, playing or singing in a formal group, discussion of recorded music, or any other musical activity.

Although **open group work** seldom deals with personal grief resolution, the atmosphere of working together and of shared concern can foster relationships that assist in subsequent ventilation of anxieties or sadness. Group work may also provide the support needed to effect change in one's life, as in Alcoholics Anonymous and Narcotics Anonymous. To join in positive music group programs has a therapeutic effect for those with depressive illness, in which depressed behavior may outlast the organic syndrome. For such situations, what has been described as "well-being therapy" is valuable (Fava, Rafanelli, Cazzaro, Conti, & Grandi, 1998), and music therapy groups provide just such a focus.

Persons with personality disorders or psychotic disorders can also benefit from turn-taking, in which there is a principle of mutual respect for opinions and an equable sharing of time and dominance. While not directly associated with grief resolution, the possible changes in attitude and behavior in such group activities can contribute to conflict resolution, and this may be helpful because conflict can be associated with grief issues.

In general hospital or community work, we can work with grief issues of various kinds in a **closed music therapy group** with a limited life. In such group work, the agenda can be set by the group or by the therapist, or it can arise spontaneously. Some topics are difficult to raise because of inner attitudes of shame or embarrassment, but group work in which there is mutual support may allow even taboo subjects to be dealt with.

In one such music therapy group, there were four women, all of them suffering from urinary incontinence following a stroke. Because of their age and their memories of childhood condemnation of "accidents," this problem had strong overtones of grief, shame, and humiliation. To deal with the matter required tact, but was helped by my own past experiences of stress incontinence during pregnancy, so that I had some clear understanding of the problem and could speak of it as "ours" rather than "yours"!

Another factor that helped acceptance of the theme was that I had been asked to write a booklet on urinary incontinence. I spoke of this and told them of thoughts of a suitable title that would indicate the topic of the leaflet but would not stigmatize the person who was seen to pick it up. The provisional title was "Will You Get There in Time?" and everyone smiled, saying how appropriate and yet acceptable this title was, and so the scene was set for serious work to proceed.

We started with music of the clients' earlier adult years, moved back to childhood music, and then discussed how it felt to now have renewed anxieties about bladder control, with the frightening thoughts of "being in one's second childhood," the common euphemism for dementia. This discussion was followed by pelvic floor exercises to improvised music, in which the "holding" time was gradually lengthened—and in this we *all* participated, including me.

At the next session, we had only been seated for a moment when one participant said, "Do you know, since last week and doing those exercises each day since, I haven't had one accident?" Her delight was infectious and the outcome of the group (over four weeks) was excellent, with significant improvement for all members. Such ideas can often be developed for other group work in grief and loss.

Shared Improvisation by the Group

There is, in my observations, a varying culture of improvisation, and one's use of the approach in therapy is influenced by each person's past history. The church organist who improvises to fill in time when the choir is late or creates a postlude by improvising on the recessional hymn may find it hard to deal with free-group improvisation. Jazz musicians improvise together, but the atmosphere is generally different from that of therapeutic improvisation. In jazz there will often be a definite rhythm, whereas in group improvisation for therapy there may be rhythmic as well as tonal ambiguity. But improvisation is helpful in palliative care for enjoyment rather than catharsis; we cannot separate completely the boundaries between fun and therapy, so jazz improvisation is therapeutic here.

Those who have previously been in a hospital where improvisation is a regular part of the music therapy program may be far more adventurous and creative than those for whom the work is new. Newcomers operate at a simple level harmonically and tonally unless they already have experience in music.

In Spain, for instance, when I was observing a teaching session that included group improvisation, the participants—to whom improvisation was entirely new—were very restricted in their rhythmic work. One woman started a strongly rhythmic pattern: //dum-di-di-dum dum//daah, daah//, and this was maintained for the whole improvisation. Yet in a German hospital I observed a group in which participants had been together for many months in a therapeutic community, where the program included weekly music group sessions. The overall creativity was wide-ranging in tone, harmony, and rhythm.

It is helpful to observe how people respond to the presence of instruments in the room as you decide how to present the idea of selecting instruments and starting improvisation. Some people move quickly toward the instruments. Some will make remarks such as, "I'm just too sad to want to play anything," "That could be good—to take my mind off things for a while," "Huh, kids' toys," or "I haven't come here to be entertained!" Others remain silently apathetic or apprehensive.

It reduces anxiety for the therapist to suggest a theme for the first improvisation, either a visualization of a scene or a feeling. Or the improvisation may start, and continue, without any named direction, and subsequent discussion of what happened in the work will be of therapeutic value. It is interesting to see the behaviors that emerge during the work: leadership dynamics, anger, sadness, peace, approach avoidance, and so on.

Relaxation with Music

Music for listening is sometimes used for relaxation in psychiatry when dealing with mourning and grief (Sekeles, 1999). It is also helpful in other problems, such as anger management, particularly for those who have a "short fuse" as a consequence of long-term alcohol abuse.

It is known, however, that a paradoxical effect can occur: relaxation methods can lead to increased agitation (Wegner, Broome, & Blomberg, 1997). This, I believe, probably occurs when profound relaxation "takes the brakes off" the normal defense strategies and permits the awareness of matters that are normally kept outside conscious thought processes. This heightens rather than allays the suppressed anxiety. We must be able to recognize the signs of distress in a group participant when the relaxation is so profound that (to some extent at least) the individual is in a state of altered consciousness, and difficult images arise that require individual work to reach resolution. Using verbal induction and the continued setting of parameters for visualization through the spoken word helps to guard against possible adverse effects in group relaxation and to ensure that the session is truly relaxing, that the mood of participants matches the mood of the music. Verbal input is included in many of the professionally prepared tapes that are available.

For individual work, the therapeutic use of visualization through guided imagery is a task requiring intensive, lengthy training and the development of particular skills, and we should not confuse simple relaxation techniques with the Bonny method of guided imagery and music (GIM), nor should we move outside our own professional boundaries of competence.

Individual Work: Eclecticism and Diversity in Practice

For most grief situations, the problems are highly individual and so are difficult to resolve in a group, but individual work allows us to adapt our approach to the client's individual needs. As work continues, we shall wonder whether it is the time to make a change and what that change should be: Is the client ready for a certain approach or would it be too challenging? Will she ever be able to use this or that approach, or would it be destructive to her inner peace? I wonder whether I am challenging her enough? *Asking too little is as harmful as asking too much.* The eclectic approach allows the possibility of adaptation in therapy as the client's thinking and behavior changes, to meet the client's changing needs.

There are several approaches in music therapy with named schools of thought, such as "Creative" and "Analytical." But, as mentioned in the preface, no single approach is all-sufficient. If the school to which we are committed does not help a client, do we continue with that approach regardless? Can we accept the idea of using another approach, or do we hand the client on to someone else? This is an ethical decision, and codes of ethics for music therapists rightly demand that we do not work outside our range of professional expertise. But an eclectic approach, used competently, allows us to change direction to meet our client's needs and saves the person the possible trauma of changing therapists.[1] The noted British psychiatrist Murray Cox writes that we should not be afraid of an eclectic approach since no one approach is always totally successful (1988, pp. 2–3).

The methods of working discussed in this book are all based upon the therapeutic alliance (Allen, Tarnoff, & Coyne, 1985; Bachelor, 1991). The alliance forms the foundation for various psychotherapies, including those described as

- insight-based, psychodynamically informed;
- supportive;
- cognitive behavior;
- counseling-type interactions;
- gestalt.[2]

I believe that the effective establishment of a therapeutic or working alliance, with any individual or group, is the foundation of all successful music therapy.

Fitting the Therapeutic Approach to the Client's Needs

Approaches in music therapy are not mutually exclusive, and the eclectic approach allows us to decide which modality is appropriate to a session, to different parts of one session, or to a series of sessions.

Factors governing our decision as we learn more about our client:

- **Psychosocial factors** in the background
- **Changes in behavior**
- New understanding of **disorders and disabilities**
- **Dependency**
- **Previous experiences in therapy**
- **Capacity for insight**
- **Factitious behavior**
- **Flight into health** (This is similar in origin to the above. A client adopts behavior that is intended to convey "Everything is now okay—no more therapy is needed." This "assumed health, fashioned by resistance, is generally short-lived," Wolberg, 1977, p. 611.)

Making Decisions

For a client who is free from psychosis, free from dementing illness, free from cognitive impairment due to brain trauma or lifelong mental retardation, and whose frontal lobes remain unimpaired by alcohol abuse, **insight-oriented and psychodynamically informed approaches** are appropriate.

There are, however, many people in residential and hospital facilities who need ongoing supportive work rather than major change-orientated interventions:

- Those whose long-term, chronic disorder is not amenable to treatment
- People who are facing death, whether in the near future or at some time in the more distant future
- Those who suffer from intermittent, treatment-resistant episodes of psychiatric disorders such as depression, bipolar disorder, or a psychotic condition
- Those with severe manifestations of schizophrenia who need to stay within protective care because they suffer from neuroleptic malignant syndrome and so cannot have their illness ameliorated by medication
- People with advanced dementing illness or dementia accompanied by behavioral disorders that make it impossible for them to be cared for at home or those whose family is unable to cope with home care
- Those who have a dementing condition in addition to a psychiatric disorder
- People with a major congenital disorder of cognition or physical disability

There are also people in the community who need ongoing supportive work:

- People requiring home visits because of severe disability or people in home-based palliative care
- Those who take part in day-care center programs

The basic concept of supportive therapy has already been mentioned.[3] *Support* can have many meanings:

- For some, music therapy, with its range of interventions, provides permanent help in extremely difficult circumstances—when support cannot be withdrawn either for patient or family, as in palliative care; in the long-term effects of a major stroke or other acquired disability; in the gradual and relentless deterioration of dementia; or in major psychotic illness, where ongoing (perhaps lifetime) support is essential, whether in repeated admissions, follow-up work in the community, or both.
- Music therapy also provides support for someone coping with a short-term need: post-operative pain, relaxation during childbirth, or cooperative work in rehabilitation with other therapists after an injury. Music

therapy can also support those coming to terms with a major change in life plans and personal independence, by cooperating in partial rehabilitation and by providing a means to self-esteem, a satisfying interest following a stroke or a major physical trauma.

- Through appropriate music therapy counseling or psychotherapeutic approaches, the discipline also supports those who are coming to terms with emotional trauma. This may take place as in-hospital intervention, formal outpatient treatment, or an after-discharge group.

Supportive therapy is particularly appropriate for those with a chronic psychiatric disorder, who run the risk that the illness is so much the focus of their everyday thinking that they are effectively paralyzed by it. Even with today's newer medications, there are some who suffer from neuroleptic malignant syndrome (Shalev, Hermesh, & Munitz, 1989) who cannot therefore benefit from any pharmaceutical measures in coping with the symptoms of their illness. This tragic syndrome therefore severely limits the possibility of insight and psychosocial change and also leads to enormous emotional and psychological pain.

One such patient described it as "doing it cold turkey," an extremely unhappy and terrifying experience. His command hallucinations and the unmitigated severity of his psychotic illness eventually led to his death by suicide, but we had worked together supportively and happily through weekly music therapy sessions for some fourteen years before this occurred.

Cognitive behavior approaches are intended to change behavior by solving problems rather than examining causes. Although this approach is essentially behavioral, it is less extreme than the strictly behaviorist approach in music therapy, in which music was often used in operant conditioning as a reward rather than as a significant and intrinsic element of therapy. Journal articles and textbooks will be found on solution-focused work as a cognitive behavior approach (Iveson, 1994; Miller, Hubble, & Duncan, 1996).

Cognitive behavior therapy (CBT) methods are included in many music therapy sessions but usually as components rather than as the only modality. For some people, such as those with treatment-resistant disorder and those with frontal lobe damage or other brain impairment, CBT methods are appropriate when nothing useful can emerge from asking, "Why...?"

Cognitive behavior work fits well with a supportive approach; it helps the client to find coping strategies that deal in practical ways with difficulties that are not amenable to change, and this in turn builds self-esteem.

Programs shared between clinical psychologist and music therapist have worked well for persons with substance dependency—where insight is lost—and for those with psychiatric disorders that are (at least for the time being) failing to respond to medication (e.g., bipolar disorder and intermittent biological depression).

The **gestalt,** or wholeness, approach used in empty-chair and other symbolic work is helpful for those, not being psychotic, who need to deal with issues from the past concerned with those who are dead. Some aspects of this work make it mandatory to use it only with those whose capacity for thought and understanding is intact, lest it be seen as "magic," or taken into a psychotic person's delusional thinking. I have also found it unhelpful in difficult relationships with those who are still alive.

Counseling or psychotherapeutic approaches include all or any of the above and also encourage the therapeutic alliance, which is, I believe, integral to the successful outcome of all music therapy in every field.

The ideas presented here have many applications. It is rare to find any approach that is suitable for a single population, for one "problem category" alone. For this reason, the techniques and methods are presented here in some detail and referred to only briefly in subsequent chapters when it seems that the technique has particular value for a particular population.

Working with an Individual

The range of possible methods included in an eclectic approach:

- Reflective improvisation stimulates insight and disclosure but also provides support for those whose problems are insoluble.
- Simple graphical work enhances understanding, support, and (if appropriate) decision-making in a quasi-cognitive behavioral approach. The concrete approach also helps people with memory loss and loss of insight.
- Shared improvisation and songwriting support emotional expression and insight and also enhance concepts of moving ahead.
- Cognitive behavior techniques in particular often empower the client to deal in realistic, practical ways with day-to-day problems, when continued focus on introspection may be harmful or when insight is lost.
- Symbolic work is possible with those people who are without delusional psychotic thinking.

Some of these methods are used in the following framework for a session.

1. Welcome the client and introduce yourself. I find it necessary to speak especially clearly when working with someone who is distressed, because concentration is frequently impaired.

2. After personal introductions, allow the client to tell you about himself.[4]

3. Listen carefully to a client's life history and have an empathic awareness of body language. These are the keys to establishing the communication

that leads to a therapeutic alliance. If possible, find out something about musical preference.

Sometimes we hear statements such as these:

- "The police dragged me in here when I wasn't doing anything wrong and the doctors pumped dope into me so I can't think straight." If the story begins thus, we suspect a paranoid episode or disorder and know the person is probably not accessible to anything except expression of anger. Our challenge will be to exercise enough control to ensure that the anger does not escalate so much that a dangerous crisis erupts.
- "Since I had that accident/stroke that left my leg and arm useless, I've been a burden to everyone and all I've wanted to do is die… and they won't *let* me!" A statement like this lets us know we are seeing depression with angry suicidality, and the referral should have told us whether this is an isolated episode or part of a long-term illness.
- "I don't know how to tell you… it has all been so difficult… things go up and down and I just feel confused… I don't even know myself what has gone wrong… I don't sleep properly and I can't think straight." This tells us that the client has so much difficulty in focusing that sketches (as a fairly concrete representation of emotion) will be helpful when combined with reflective improvisation and significant items of music.
- If the person pours out all the story readily with memories of events and relationships coming easily to the surface, perhaps giving us the feeling that matters are being revealed that have long been held back, it is inappropriate to interrupt and suggest changing to music; this can wait for a while.

4. Although we respond verbally to what we have been told, music is vitally important here, usually but not invariably at the end of the life story. On many occasions it is a *familiar item* of music that is associated with a lost relationship, such as the songs a mother sang to a child who subsequently died, music of courtship recalled in bereavement and played to facilitate the expression of held-back emotions, and so on. However wide our repertoire, there are times when we need to play an item that we do not know. Sometimes the client can sing it, but often the best we can do is to say, "Can you tell me why the song is so important? I will try to get it for you for next week, but I cannot promise that I'll be able to!" Improvised music is also important here, to reflect back to the client a sense of being understood, validating the emotions that have been expressed or that remained below the surface.[5] Our observations of the client's behavior while the improvised music is played are also informative.

5. The improvisation may lead on to disclosure of deeper needs than those previously disclosed. Avoid accepting instructions for secrecy. We then

need some discussion, summary, and feedback from the client so that we can learn how the improvisation was perceived.

- Was it a good representation of what the person feels, what life has been like?
- Was it revealing something to the client of which he had not previously been aware?
- Did he hear something in the music that we were not aware of including, did he project onto the music some difficult and unacknowledged emotion?
- Was it all wrong, nothing like what he was feeling? This too can inform us!

6. In many sessions the client will improvise alone or (unless there is a reason for not doing so) together with the therapist. Either way, the interpretation of that music should be verified by the therapist as to its meaning for the client or patient. As already discussed, meaning is not universal, but is strongly affected by culture and psychopathology.

   It is important to recognize that disclosure of difficult material is not the only goal of therapy but a hurdle to be negotiated and the disclosed material used for maximum benefit to the patient (Cox, 1988, p. 4). I realized this some twenty years ago when a man (hospitalized because of physical illness) told many stories of his own wartime heroism; these were found to be untrue, and a provisional diagnosis was made of Munchausen syndrome. He was, however, not confronted on this, and instead a supportive approach was adopted in an attempt to deal with the need that led to his tall stories, the (verified) major cruelty and rejection he had suffered in childhood.

   The psychiatrist who was caring for him asked me to become involved. After several counseling sessions including improvised music, came the disclosure. "You know, Ruth, none of those stories were true." This disclosure was not the goal of therapy but the first crucial step toward validation of his unhappiness and need for self-esteem. To stop at the disclosure, perceiving it as the goal of our work together, would have been both useless and unethical.

   Furthermore, the person who most needs the "newly-discovered" material is the client (Cox, 1988, p. 6), and it has long been my practice to say, "It is not so much that *I* need to know what has been happening—it's *you* who need to know!"

7. From here on, the order of events is determined entirely by the progress in the session, the client's responses or disclosures, our estimate of his capacity for change, and the number of sessions we expect to have.

8. When there is expectation that the client will return for another session, the separation is a low-key matter, with some discussion of
- date and time of next session;
- preparation for that session (compose words for a song, do a life road map, write a poem, draw a sketch);
- any special plans for the week (e.g., a visit home, visit by relatives or friends, job interviews, plans for going with the social worker to see new accommodation, etc.).

These plans may influence how the subsequent sessions go, and we must note what is planned, so that next week we can ask, "How did the interview for that job go?" or "How did you get on with the social worker when you went to look at that boarding house?" If events were disappointing, it is important that they are dealt with in our session, probably through improvised music and sketches.

Discuss suicide if this seems remotely possible (it is known that discussion does not increase the likelihood of death, Morgan, 1994), phrasing the question obliquely ("Some people get so down about the future that they lose interest in living. Does that sound like you?"). Our actions will depend upon the words and style of the reply. It is helpful to set up a contract to stay alive until next session; my practice is to add, "And that does *not* mean you have my permission to kill yourself when our session next week is over!" This comment is usually met with a smile or even with laughter but with recognition that this is not a joke.

It is useful to read about aspects of suicidal behavior that may indicate risk, so as to reduce one's natural anxiety in dealing with the possibility of self-killing. The article by Mann and his colleagues (Mann, Waternaux, Haas, & Malone, 1999) is particularly useful because it includes 118 references on the topic.

The final component of any session will be the use of the theme song, usually chosen by the client in the initial session. This song is a reminder of the session content until the next appointment.

9. Writing accurate notes in the clinical file is an aspect of music therapy that is vitally important.

If we are fortunate enough to work in a facility where integrated notes[6] are used, we know there is a good chance people will read what we write and our notes may even become a top priority for other staff to read before talking with the patient in question. If, however, our notes are written in a separate "music therapy" section at the back of the folder, we may be less certain that our comments will be read by others unless we have achieved a team relationship in which music therapy is seen as something more than recreation.

Nevertheless, however many doubts we have that our comments will be read, we must write an accurate account of our interventions. We ourselves need to be able to look back and assess the rate of progress. If we wish to write about our work, it is helpful to have clear notes to which we can refer. Although a rare occurrence, the notes may also be needed for legal reasons. Our notes also show that the session took place.

After the session ends, we also alert other staff to difficult matters emerging from the session, in case the person seeks further help during the evening or before next session, or if suicide or decompensation are seen as possible risks.

Practical Approaches in Eclectic Work

A session with a client or patient normally starts with verbal interaction. This is because people who have little previous experience of creating music are shy of doing so at the beginning of the first session and personal expression through music is often ambiguous—and will remain a mystery to the therapist until we understand more of the individual's cultural and psychological makeup.

As we prepare to write notes in the file and look back over the session just completed, we shall probably find ourselves thinking about the meaning of the music in the context of the general interaction. What did it mean to the client when so-and-so happened? What did it mean to me when the client played this-or-that? What does the shared improvisation tell me about how the program is going? How well did my reflective improvisation validate the client's sense of being understood?

Sometimes success in sharing music together comes more easily than expected; a very serious-minded and severely depressed woman, grieving over an abortion from many years before, willingly sat down on the floor opposite me when I had just seated myself cross-legged, with an Indian ceramic pot-drum on a cotton "doughnut" between my knees. She then played intricate rhythms that complemented mine, smiling with greater ease than I had seen at our introductory session the week before. The posture was so unexpected to her that she behaved more naturally in our shared "jam session" than I had ever seen before, and we shared in the laughter as we both got stiffly to our feet afterward. Paradoxically, our shared laughter facilitated the subsequent work on painful matters from her personal life.

In shared (rather than reflective) improvisation in the context of a one-to-one session, some clients feel more comfortable sitting at the keyboard with the therapist rather than playing a percussion instrument.[7] Usually I play at the bass end and leave the client the top. I suggest that the client uses only the black keys. Using only the black keys ensures that there are no discords of any magnitude and, depending upon which of the five notes is made the "home note" (the tonic or keynote), the emotional content can be varied.

The stereotype in music that minor equals sad and major equals happy is untenable. However, we do find that a melody played exclusively on the black notes and using D# or A# as the tonic is more likely to be perceived as being sad by the musically naive than a melody that uses F# as the tonic—which is commonly perceived as happy or positive—although this will depend upon the tempo at which the melody is played.

Sometimes emotions emerge that threaten to overwhelm the client, and in this situation the holding nature of the accompaniment is vitally important if we are to avoid decompensation and a psychic crisis. At one such session, anger threatened to be overwhelming and, since the patient had been admitted because of acute suicidality, it was important to contain the situation. I played the holding chords in the bass more loudly and adopted a strong rhythm; the agitation and anger that were apparent in the patient's previous playing diminished rapidly. As we drew to a close, she turned and said, "Wow, I thought the anger was going to get away from me for a while back there!"

It is essential that after the music is complete we talk with the client about how it felt. We must never assume our own interpretation of the client's musical behavior is 100 percent accurate. What appears to symbolize aggression may in fact represent determination or if it is anger it may be the client's anger with self, anger with the music therapist, anger with the illness, anger with God, anger with the medical profession for failing to effect a cure, anger with another staff member, or any one of a number of causes. We cannot jump to conclusions.

Songwriting

The depressed or withdrawn client, the musically illiterate, the person with bad "vibes" about music dating from school days, may find the suggestion of original composition terrifying or repulsive. Yet we know that writing one's feelings and thoughts into a song assists expressivity and enhances the possibility of a good outcome. So what do we do?

The simplest and least-challenging initiation into creativity in song is parody or word substitution. This process has a long history—many of us are familiar with the song "How Deep Is the Night" set to the melody of a piano étude by Chopin, or the childhood parodies on sections of the "Toreadors' Song" from Bizet's *Carmen.* (Our favorite was "O Je-mi-ma, look at your Uncle Jim, he's in the duckpond learning how to swim," but there were others, less appropriate for publication!)

In one maximum-security psychiatric ward of forty years ago, when staff were poorly trained and perceived more as guards than nurses, a frequent request was for the song "John Brown's Body." In one verse, the men substituted the name of their most-disliked charge nurse as the person to be hanged on the tree! (I was never quite sure of the ethics of assisting in that song. Was I encouraging antistaff violence or giving a healthy outlet for natural feelings? I settled for the second but was careful who was near when the song was sung.)

In music therapy for grief, there is a real need for songwriting. It encourages personal creativity. The use of melody gives added emotional color to the words. Songwriting allows manageable catharsis and supports the expression in poetic form of thoughts that may be taboo in ordinary conversation. The song becomes the client's personal possession. Preparing a good-quality copy is important. The song can become a transitional object to take from the session into the future as a reinforcement and reminder of past achievements in therapy.

On some occasions it has been impossible to facilitate the writing of a song by the client in an early session, usually because of a depressive illness, and yet the provision of a song as an active component in treatment is required. In those circumstances, the composition of a song by the therapist alone is not only acceptable but necessary.

Vignette: Andrew, His Depression and His Song

Andrew had been hospitalized for some weeks, and although in theory his depressive illness had waned, his behavior remained depressed. After interdisciplinary discussion, I was asked to become involved and decided to use a cognitive behavior approach. There are many accounts in the literature of the need for strategies to deal with depressed behavior that outlasts the acute illness, and "well-being" therapy has been recommended (Fava et al, 1998). Although these writers did not include music therapy, the applications of our work in this situation are obvious.

I knew Andrew well from group music therapy in the psychogeriatric assessment ward, so it was not difficult to establish an alliance with him on an individual basis, since he already trusted me not to push him too far. As we talked about his life, his need for an improved self-image was clearly the top priority so I composed for him "The OK Song." The simplicity of the melody and rhythm were designed to make the song easily recalled and to make the idea contained in it, focusing on self-acceptance, easy to remember. Bartlett, in his innovative study of memory, emphasized the value of rhythm in assisting recall (Bartlett, 1932, p. 270).

I have since used this song for many other people who were unable initially to write songs for themselves and who needed a simple approach to morale building. Those who have benefited have included persons with schizophrenia and similar disorders, depression in various forms, substance misuse, mania and

This song has been useful with many persons suffering from depression (whether as a major depressive illness, as one phase of a bipolar disorder, or when depression accompanies a psychotic illness, substance dependency, or other conditions). It is to be accompanied by the therapist initially and later used by the patient alone to reinforce the content of the therapy session.

hypomania, and bipolar disorder. This song I "prescribed" to be sung at least six times each day—not necessarily out loud, except in the shower where nobody would notice. The idea of singing the song inside one's head is readily accepted since most of us have had the experience of having a tune running through the mind.

In composing a song for a client

- focus on the main issues;
- use plain language;
- create a melody that is within the compass of the voice of that individual and readily singable—not great leaps but stepwise melodic movement;
- keep the song short if you want the words to be remembered.

Some clients will be able to compose their own songs by writing the words and discussing the type of music to be composed, trying it out with the music therapist until a satisfactory creation is achieved. If permissible, record this on tape, create a simple accompaniment, and then either put it on paper, record it on tape with the client singing the melody line, or both. Give the finished product to the client to keep. Some clients will be able to create the entire song, singing it or playing the notes of the melody on the keyboard while the therapist writes it down by dictation onto music manuscript paper or records it on tape, if this is ethically permitted.

This should be subsequently transferred to paper, with an appropriate accompaniment as discussed during the session. If possible do this via a computer program that produces an elegant printout of the music with all the details of title, composer, tempo, words fitted correctly in syllables under the notes, and so on. The finished product should be given to the client to keep.

Two Vignettes: Client's Creativity

- One young woman, who said she was musically illiterate, agreed to try putting some thoughts about the future into a song. She sat at the keyboard while I fetched a book of manuscript paper from another room and in those few minutes had (as she put it) invented a simple melody on an arpeggio basis with words expressing hope and determination to be happy. This was in marked contrast to her earlier suicidal depression and was the moment at which she expressed the idea that she could be happy for the first time in several years.

  At home that evening I transferred the hastily written song from paper to the computer, with all the musical details of tempo and dynamics plus a simple accompaniment and a large-print heading at the top, giving name of song, composer, and date. Two copies were sent to her by fax to the ward—one for her and one for her file. It was then used by other clinicians in their interviews in the week before I saw her again, and the song proved to be a useful link to her discharge home.

- Another young woman, suffering for several years from a disabling bipolar disorder, had started to deal with her anger about the illness and its destructive effects upon her career and marriage through shared improvisation. The cognitive behavior approach had been useful for her. Comparatively she began to think dispassionately about the impact of the illness on her life, working out strategies for living—in which the work was shared between the clinical psychologist who used a CBT approach and me. This insight had been hard-won; the difficulties of a shared improvisation, in which her anger became almost unmanageable, were described earlier in this chapter.

  At one such shared session, she spontaneously sang a song about her life and its challenges. She was able to sing it to me several times so that I could get it down on paper. Interestingly (and she commented on this spontaneously), in a previous admission she had composed songs that vented her anger but had not allowed me to write them down. This comment provided an interesting lead into discussion on the therapeutic alliance and self-trust, self-esteem, change, and determination. Again, the song was prepared properly and given to her, thereafter becoming a valued possession and a reminder of freedom to express ideas.

We should not assume that clients who are unmusical are unable to create their own meaningful songs. Even a chant on a single note can become a thing of beauty when the therapist adds harmonic structure in the accompanying chords. The example given below, a song of despair on middle C, demonstrates this. Note that this may be a response to bereavement by death or another loss of intimate relationship, but is also experienced when termination of therapy has been handled badly or when the client's dependency needs remain unmet. Such words may indicate a wish for suicide, perhaps actual plans for death, and we should be aware of this possibility—responsive to it.

SONG OF DESPAIR

Voice
I am so sad, now I'm a - lone, I feel I can't go on, now that he's gone.
Piano

Those who are unfamiliar with music may find it hard to imagine that they could successfully compose their own songs, but if there have already been times of sharing the keyboard, the task is made easier. The ability of the therapist to write the song down rapidly makes the task less daunting.

These brief vignettes provide ideas as to the possible variants of songwriting, whether by therapist alone, client alone, or in cooperation. The main points are these:

- Be sure your skills in writing music down from informal dictation are well honed, unless you are allowed to record the session. In that case you can play and replay the recording in private while you get the notes onto paper or the computer.
- Wait until the client's self-confidence is at a reasonable level, lest the songwriting becomes yet another failure.
- Play some familiar songs that have simple melodies as an introduction to songwriting; it doesn't have to be complex to "work"!
- Discuss ideas and moods that the client may wish to put into the words and music.
- Allow the client to be alone with the keyboard for a few moments. Leave the room, if this is not contravening required supervision, or move to another part of the room to write notes, look up a book on the shelf, or whatever.
- When the moment arrives, keep everything at low tension if possible so that the experience is perceived as enjoyable, interesting, cathartic, fun, and not a terrible demand.

My own view is that songs by the therapist alone are to be avoided unless circumstances of physical or mental health make it impossible for the client to participate. Such songs can, however, be valued as a gift from therapist to client, and in palliative care may become the treasured possession of those who are left.

Songs created by the client are important in many ways. They are a personal possession, a personal achievement, an expression of thoughts that are otherwise difficult to express, and so on. They are also useful to the therapist in providing a marker of progress, an indicator of mood, and a step in our working, collaborative alliance.

Graphic Representation

My own abilities are so meager that I hesitate to describe it as "art" but it works. As I have said elsewhere (Bright, 1999b), the fact that I am not a gifted artist can help the client, particularly someone who has had a long illness, for whom a feeling of superiority over a staff member is a rare and enjoyable experience.

For this work, it is helpful if there is a large whiteboard in the room where the session takes place. The work on the board is always supplemented by a large scribble pad of plain paper, so one can give a copy of what was drawn to the client to take from the session.

Why draw things anyway? My first use of sketches was with a German tourist who had suffered a crisis in a flight to Australia and was apparently psychotic on arrival at Sydney Airport. He had been brought by ambulance from the airport to the psychiatric admission unit, and I was asked to do an immediate assessment to see whether there was anything I could do until the interpreter arrived in the afternoon. He spoke no English and I spoke almost no German, so, until the arrival of the professional interpreter, music therapy seemed the obvious answer!

I started with my repertoire of German traditional songs, including some childhood songs such as "*Fuchs du hast die ganz gestollen*" (a humorous song about the fox stealing the goose), which can bring back memories of family life and lead to further disclosure, but in this case, apart from a slight smile, there was no major reaction. I then went on to play and sing "*Die Lorelei*", which includes the words "*Ich weiss nicht... das ich so traurig bin*" (I do not know... why I am so sad). Some people say that this song is associated with Nazism, but in my experience this is less important than the associations with sadness and nostalgia. The response was immediate, with heightened alertness and eye contact, and various comments that were, sadly, unintelligible to me. I immediately went to the whiteboard on the wall of the room and drew three faces—one happy, one sad, and one angry.

I then pointed to these in turn, and using a questioning gesture invited the young man to point to the face that matched his feelings. He chose first the sad one, then with an angry gesture the picture of the angry face. Our session went on from these, with improvisation to express those feelings, and although it did not lead to major disclosures, it decreased his agitation and gave the staff some idea of how he was feeling while they waited for the interpreter to come.

Since that time I have used sketches in most sessions, usually after trust has been established through reflective improvisation, as in the assessment described in chapter 1, but earlier on in the work if there are language difficulties. Such difficulties arise not only because of ethnicity but also in alexithymia, in which there is a profound difficulty in finding words to describe emotions (Kirkmayer & Robbins, 1993).

Sketches are also helpful when there are organic causes for difficulties with words, for example, in aphonia resulting from a brainstem lesion or dysarthria from other brain damage.[8] Sketches combined with reflective or shared improvisation are also enormously useful in aphasia, when the nondominant hemisphere, the locus of control (in general terms) of artistic creativity, is intact, even though verbal communication is impaired or wiped out completely. Sketches and reflective improvisation together have transformed the atmosphere and the client, on many occasions.

Which face is the real you?

1. The face or faces selected give an indication of how the work will proceed. In recent years I have added a face showing horror, similar to the famous picture called *The Scream* by the Norwegian artist Munch, and although on one occasion a young woman interpreted this (as a defense, it seemed) as a cartoon character "the friendly ghost," this interpretation has remained unique. Others have found the additional face to be a source of expressivity and even comforting—perhaps because, by its very presence in the sketch, it gives permission to acknowledge fear. The face representing fear has so far never evoked an exacerbation of fear but rather a feeling of relief. (There is perhaps an analogy here with the fact that discussion of possible suicide brings relief, lessening rather than increasing the likelihood of death [Morgan, 1994].)

But faces are only one use of graphics in therapy. Other sketches are described below. All these sketches have been used over many years, and clients often comment on their value in helping them understand the past as well as helping to show the way ahead.

Is it safe to open it up and have a look inside?

2. The locked chest with forbidden feelings: Is it safe to open the lid? This sketch is such a powerful image that many people have needed equally powerful reassurance that the hinge is such that the lid can only be opened a very small distance and that the client is able to shut it as soon as it becomes too difficult to keep it open. This sketch, with the words written onto it by the client, provides helpful material for shared improvisation and songwriting.

Some people carry a real burden through life.

3. The figure with the load on its back: What is in that load? Writing the words in gives the client permission to put in whatever is necessary. Sometimes the list spills over the sides of the load so that we end up with a long line of words, as with a young woman who had been the victim of incest and exploitation. She wrote: *fear, exploitation, rape, pain, disbelief, anger, failure, distrust, poverty, violence, helplessness,* and *self-loathing.* The sketch and the conversation that ensue, are then used for further improvisation, both reflective and shared.
4. The set of ten steps that has been described and illustrated on page 17 (Bright, 1986, 1999b) was originally devised for those with frontal-lobe deficits whose thinking is usually in the concrete rather than the abstract, but since then it has been used for many others. These were described in chapter 1.

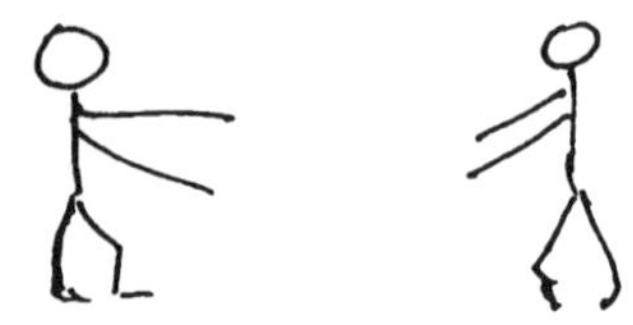

What do you think is happening, and what will happen next?

5. A sketch of two stick figures of indeterminate gender facing each other with hands outstretched provides a test similar to the (Murray) Thematic Apperception Tests. "What do you think is happening?" leads to widely differing replies.

   One middle-aged woman, suffering from apparently intractable bulimia, added a third figure, of a child in a dress standing with one arm outstretched toward each of the other figures, and she then wrote underneath: "Please stop fighting and love me." This sketch provided material for deeper understanding of the etiology of her difficulties, more intense improvisation, songwriting, and the drawing of a life road map.

   If the sketch has suggested conflict between specified people, it can be useful to extend it to start building a wall between the two figures, asking, "What do you think came between them?" The blocks in the wall can then be labeled and the developing understanding that emerges from the sketch can be used as the basis for extended improvisation in stages, followed by further discussion.

   If the situation is such that the client may be able to effect change, then strategies for change would be included in that improvisation. If change is impossible, then the improvisation that follows would be focused on acceptance, separation, or whatever is appropriate.

   This sketch, like several others used in this work, is similar to the Thematic Apperception approach of Murray (1943) in that the client interprets the picture in accordance with personal motivation and personal pressures. Writing on the Thematic Apperception Test, Gieser and Stein (1999, p. 6) comment that evaluation tests interfere with the possibility of establishing rapport with the patient, whereas the interpretation of pictures is part of therapy.

   The stick figures I use have similar value, contributing to the establishment of a therapeutic alliance because the interpretation, combined with improvised music work, is all part of therapy. The sketches even appear to have some advantages over formal pictures presented on cards (as in the Thematic Apperception Test). Because the sketches are done by the therapist on the whiteboard, the client can change the figures, add to them, or erase a figure. It also seems to be less essential for the client to identify with one figure in the given picture. The possibility of adding to the sketch enables the viewer to enter into it as a character not shown in the original sketch. This may prove helpful. A further advantage is that the figures are without gender and—as far as possible—without cultural bias or even cultural identity, making the pictures more nearly universal.

The balance of our lives can change quite a lot. How is yours right now?

6. An old-fashioned set of scales, with a pan on each side hanging from a horizontal beam across the top. This has been an extraordinarily evocative image. The pans can be drawn at different positions of balance or imbalance and used in different symbolism, depending upon the needs of the individual.

   The client may draw people standing in the two pans and use that as a way of dealing with dominance and subservience in difficult relationships. The sketch also gives a good basis for musical improvisation, whether by the therapist, by the client, or shared.

7. Putting things away in the cupboard. We know that dealing with issues from the past does not mean forgetting them. Depressed behavior can continue after the illness is over, and difficult memories from the past can haunt us, sometimes justifying the descriptor post-traumatic stress disorder. Can we develop ways of dealing with the painful past, neither denying it nor letting it become the focus of our life and relationships?

   To deal with past trauma by using a simple sketch of a locked cupboard and a person walking away putting the key in his or her pocket may seem too easy to be believable. But of course, the sketch itself is only a reminder and a concrete representation of a deeper emotional experience. This may arise from a visit to the cemetery, from letting the ashes of an angry letter float downstream, from writing a song about past and present, or any other appropriate action—an action that is the more memorable for being linked with music. The significance of the lock on the door and the pocketing of the key is that one is able to go back and have a look if one needs it. The past is not blotted out, but simply placed under one's own control.

Assigning Homework Preparation

We know that active involvement and collaboration with the therapist contribute to good outcome (Mackenzie, 1988). I have found it helpful to ask the client to do some work between sessions. I confess that people do not always remember to do it, but those who do so benefit. We may learn something useful from those who do not. It may indicate memory impairment, avoidant behavior, an overloaded schedule, a transference issue, our own failure to establish an alliance, or an attempt at sabotaging treatment or splitting.

The **life road map,** which illustrates the pivotal incidents and relationships, the ups and downs of life—as perceived by the client—may be done during a session or as preparation for a subsequent session. It may be a single sheet of paper with a few incidents, each labeled with a date and clearly leading either up or down. One young man used a single page to show the effects of his mother's death and father's remarriage on his life; he drew a gravestone in close proximity to wedding bells and a child at the bottom of the page curled up in a fetal posture.

It may, however, be considerably longer and more complex. One young woman, a university graduate, heroin user, sex worker in both the heterosexual and the homosexual trade, the victim of childhood incest and teenage rape, and not surprisingly in view of this disclosure, ambivalent about her own sexuality used seven sheets of continuous paper towelling to draw her road map of life, and even so needed to finish it on the back of the last sheet!

The road maps were illustrated with the key incidents and relationships and showed the lifeline moving up or down, gradually or steeply, as the history dictated. In both instances they provided material for musical creativity and expressivity in improvisation, songwriting, and movement with music, as well as the basis for informed verbal therapy.

Other preparation for sessions can include writing a **poem** to be set to music as a song, writing a **letter,** drawing a **sketch,** and keeping a **journal** which need not be shown to the therapist. Discussion may include the content, or what it was like to write the letter, to draw the picture, or to maintain the journal.

All these require effort, commitment, and determination from the client. It is important not to be the Angry Teacher if the work is not done, but a useful discussion can evolve whether or not the preparation has been done.

Empty-Chair Work

Introductory Comments

Empty-chair work is sometimes appropriate for those who are failing to cope with feelings of guilt following a bereavement by death. In my view, however, it is such a powerful experience for the client that it should generally be used only if assessment has been done and avoided if there is less than an hour available for the procedure. It is usually appropriate only with people who have been admitted for in-patient care because it is essential that professional support is available afterward if required, and because of the risks of impaired concentration if the person has to drive home or even cross a busy street!

Not only is it important that we know what we are doing, we ourselves also need professional supervision available for debriefing afterward in addition to interdisciplinary discussion.

Benefits

Empty-chair work can provide

- a sense of release from guilty feelings;
- relief at having said things that had not previously been spoken;
- diminished anger with the deceased but also with life in general;
- diminished misuse of addictive substances;
- improved relationships with the living.

I have never used this as an abreactive technique. There is no probing as to the past, although explanations and discussion often follow the experience, and the client is in control. It is therefore improbable that a therapist-led dialogue will elicit false memories, although the client does have the possibility of spontaneously challenging the deceased on real sexual abuse.

Empty-chair work is contraindicated when there is a belief in magic and the occult, dementia, loss of insight due to frontal-lobe dysfunction, mental retardation, acute psychosis, or delusions (also called "ideas") of reference, in which people believe that ordinary events have a special meaning unique to themselves. Once a decision has been made to use the empty-chair technique, we must find out whether there is any music associated with the lost person or lost relationship so we can find that item before the new session actually takes place. **The associated music is a crucial factor in the reality of the work that follows.**

Procedure

Beforehand: If you have decided in advance to use the method, tell the primary nurse or other staff member who has a close working relationship with the client that a session of empty-chair work is planned. Ensure that support will be available if the client needs to talk further about matters that emerge.

In your consulting room you need three chairs. Arrange two of these about 2 meters apart, facing one another with a space to one side so you should be within sight if the client needs reassurance of your presence, but in such a position that there is no interruption to the client's eye-line to the empty chair. The musical instrument that is to be used—usually a keyboard, Autoharp, or guitar—must be placed where it is easily accessible at all phases of the session.

1. Talk to the person about the awful burden of guilt.
2. Explain how empty-chair work is done. Reassure the person that
   - it is only symbolic, no ghost is present;
   - no real communication takes place with the dead;
   - it is simply a way of saying the words we wish we had said, imagining

how the person might have responded, and seeing deeper into oneself—the relationship regrets, disappointments, and anger.

3. Explain the steps:
- "I shall play some music to help you get into the right mood. It will be (the title), which may help you think about your feelings about (name the person)."
  - "I shall then ask you to speak directly to that empty chair, just as you would if the person were really there."
  - "Then you move to the other chair and speak on behalf of that other person."
  - "Then you will move back into the first chair, and I will 'put you back together again'" (or use whatever phraseology is appropriate to the person's own style of speech).
  - "Last of all we will talk a little about how that was for you and improvise some music together."
  - "I am sure it all sounds quite different from what we usually do in music therapy, but if you agree to take part in this, I think you will find you feel a whole lot better afterward, as other people have with whom I have worked."
  - Allow a few moments of silence and be ready to answer further questions. We are not bulldozing people into something they will later regret. But usually the idea of empty-chair work brings a feeling of relief that there is something that can be done.

4. Assuming the client has agreed to be involved in the approach, go straight into music to support these ideas. Here one hopes that the music may lead to further insight, possible disclosure, and the beginnings of self-forgiveness, but in any case it will probably validate the feelings expressed by the client, or the feelings we have sensed but that were not overtly revealed.
5. Allow just a few moments of silence. There may be further verbal interchange but it is not essential and if it does occur it should come spontaneously from the client, not from the therapist.
6. Modulate as necessary to appropriate keys as you move between familiar and improvised music. The person will probably not need verbal reminders of the selected familiar items. But reminders can be given if the person looks puzzled.
7. "Now speak to that empty chair as if (name the person) were sitting there. Remember there is nobody there, but just imagine there is." What happens next will reveal to you the extent to which this procedure is going to work. If the client turns to you and says, "Oh, well I think I'd say..."

then one may as well let the plan go, because there is too much resistance to allow things to proceed. But if the client remains facing the empty chair and speaks in terms of "you" and "your" and often in a tone of voice that is different from the normal speaking tone, then we may hope for a useful outcome.

8. When the client seems to have finished, at least for the time being, ask the client to move to the opposite chair and speak for the other person. Again, the style of speech that follows indicates the likelihood of good outcome. If the client turns to you and says, "But I've no idea what to say!" then we know that is better to stop than persevere with a meaningless routine. In this case, we need to speak in such a way as to avoid blaming the client or suggest that there was a failure, and instead reassure the client that it is difficult to do this work and that we can find another way of providing support. What does indicate the possibility of good outcome is when the client's voice changes to resemble what one assumes to be the voice of the dead person.
9. This process may require a further "conversation," but often one turn in each chair is sufficient before returning to the original position.
10. When the client has returned to the original position, we must de-role him or her. "You have done really well, but I want you now to become aware again of the room. You are sitting facing an empty chair, and you have spoken as if you were talking to (name the person), but it has only been an imagined conversation, what you wish you could have said. There is nobody else here except you and me—no ghosts or spirits, just you and me." Extend this return to reality as long as seems necessary to achieve the change without haste. "Can you turn your chair around toward me now, so we can work together for a few more minutes?"
11. No suggestions can be given for the last phase. It will depend entirely upon what has transpired in the "conversation" and on the skills and empathy of the therapist.

I have never found that a situation has become worse through this work. This may indicate the care taken in deciding whether or not the method is appropriate for the person concerned, but it may be that clients for whom it would be traumatic refused to enter into the scenario. Refusals have been rare, perhaps because those to whom it is offered have reached the end of their rope and grasp at anything that offers hope of change.

Whatever the outcome, the client must be supported in this. Support can consist of shared improvisation, songwriting, further reflective improvisation, the selection of a theme to take from the session, or a repetition of the theme chosen during assessment, together with additional supportive verbal interaction.

12. One should plan and discuss arrangements for a follow-up session, not of repeated empty-chair work but for review and possible separation. It is also essential to remind the client of support available from other clinicians before the music therapist returns to the unit, saying the staff member concerned knows there may be a need for one-to-one conversation.

Then write the session up in the client's file. If possible talk personally with the psychiatrist or other significant clinician and the person from whom support may be needed that evening.

This type of work can achieve excellent outcome (see vignettes in chapter 5). It seems probable that, by such work, we are putting the client in control so that memories are modified within the brain, becoming manageable, and are no longer a source of trauma simply in the act of recall.

By providing symbolic work, we give the person an opportunity for taking control of life—offering an apology, expressing anger, saying farewell to the deceased—and although this can only be imaginal, it affects the mind profoundly. It may be that there are some parallels here with the eye-movement desensitization and reprocessing advocated by Shapiro, since she notes that stimuli other than eye movements such as tones and rhythmic tapping can be used effectively (Shapiro, 1998).

Other Symbolic Work: Saying Good-bye to the Dead

Visits to the site of interment or, if no grave site exists, a visit to a significant place, are usefully combined with music therapy. Saying good-bye, thank you, or please forgive me helps achieve resolution of a difficult bereavement.

Although the work can be done in imagination in the consulting room, an actual visit to the appropriate place is useful. It is not difficult to provide appropriate music, by singing, playing a guitar, an Autoharp, or another portable instrument. If there is a need for a significant recording use a battery-operated tape or CD player.

In one such instance the patient who had been hospitalized with depression sang the song at the graveside that she had promised to sing at her sister's funeral, but had been unable because of her own illness at the time (Bright, 1994).

In another instance at the graveside, a grieving young mother buried a page containing the song she had written for her dead child and sang that song softly before returning to the hospital car, where I sat awaiting her return. Another young woman sang to her dead child and buried the only object of value that she owned—a gold signet ring—at the foot of the tiny gravestone.

Careful preparation for a visit to the grave site is essential, including discussion with colleagues and the client. A frequent part of the procedure is to suggest that the client writes a letter to the deceased, in which many thoughts can be set out beforehand, to avoid the possibility of the client realizing after returning from the visit that some vital matter has been omitted. This letter is then normally burned at the grave. The ashes may be scrabbled into the gravel beside the grave, into the soil of a memorial garden if there is not formal interment site, or allowed to drift away on the surface of a river or the ocean.

Although this method, like empty-chair work, can provide only symbolic communication with the dead, it does bring great relief to many clients. It enables them, not to forget the past, but to "put it away in the cupboard," as described in item 7 above under Graphic Representation.

The session after the grave site visit will include graphic work, songwriting, and improvisation to reinforce what was achieved at the grave. If time permits and the client is not too emotionally drained to allow it to be useful, this follow-up work is most helpful if done immediately on return to the facility, while matters are still clear in the mind for both. But if this is impossible, we should try to arrange for a suitable person to be available with whom the client can talk things over.

When planning such an intervention, it is essential that the music therapist does not accept dual responsibility for driving the car and for supporting the client. We should not be shocked if anger emerges—anger with the deceased for having abandoned the survivor, anger with what took place during the person's life (this is common after incest and other difficult relationships), or anger with the self for not having done something important.

Scattering the ashes on the water at the seashore or in a river, with imaginal conversation with the deceased, has proven helpful to many. One young mother, only in her late thirties, whose two teenage children had died, one from a motorbike accident and one from a drug overdose, had difficulty in acknowledging her anger with both of them for their behavior that led to death. Disclosing and dealing with this anger was a large part of her music therapy management within the consulting room, and the scattering of ashes was a family affair rather than a therapeutic intervention. By chance I saw her some years later, and she said, "You know you told me to go and put the ashes on the water? You wouldn't believe how much it helped!"

Imaginal work is also helpful for those who are unable to visit the grave because of disability or distance. Beryl, a middle-aged widow, had become quadriplegic as the result of a clot following an angiogram, not long after her husband's death, and was in a nursing home. After several sessions she disclosed that although they had been happy together, she felt relieved at his death. He had always been the popular partner, and she felt herself to be the unwanted extra at any party.

When he died, she felt horrified that her first thought had been "Perhaps now they'll notice *me* for a change!" She wondered whether the paralysis was a punishment for that response, tried to forget her marriage, and refused to listen to tapes of music they had shared that were brought in by friends.

After both familiar and improvised music and counseling, Beryl realized that her perceptions were "off" as she expressed it, that he had not tried to put her down or present her as unimportant. We knew she could not go to the cemetery to express any of this, so music was used to set the scene for visualization of the grave site. She imagined herself going there to ask forgiveness and thank her husband for the happy years they had spent together. When she spoke to him, I moved away from the bed so she had privacy, and I continued to play very softly so that I did not hear what she was saying. Later she expressed relief about the experience. I de-roled her and we ended with low-tension familiar music.

The results were particularly interesting. Improvement was reported to me by nursing staff before our next session. I was told that she had returned to listening to music, was less irritable and depressed, and had started to talk warmly of her late husband. "What on earth did you do to make such a change?" My answer was that the changes were made by Beryl herself. I merely provided the milieu and music through which change could take place!

Imaginal work in the music room has proven useful for persons who have lost a baby—before birth (including death by abortion), at birth, or in the neonatal period. The music therapist asks what lullaby was sung, or what the parent wishes he or she could have sung to the child. Next, as with other similar procedures, the therapist emphasizes the symbolic nature of the work and asks the parent to imagine holding the baby in his or her arms, looking down toward the child's face, and feeling the weight of the child—perhaps very little weight if the child died before birth or was very premature. This can be of crucial importance.

The lullaby is then sung by the therapist (I use the Autoharp for this because it provides gentle and unobtrusive support), and the parent may or may not feel able to join in. We should never imply that for the intervention to work the parent must sing too.

The parent may also wish to speak to the dead child to ask forgiveness, express sadness at the child not having survived, or say whatever seems important or necessary. Then the music is played again but gradually fades away until there is silence. What is said next is usually the decision of the parent, but the music therapist can speak quietly about the relief the client may experience and otherwise bring the session gently to a close once it is clear that no more needs to be said. Sometimes a formal session follows, but sometimes the symbolic farewell is all that is required.

After any of these symbolic interventions, we may need to invite the client to stay in the room alone for a few minutes before facing the outside world again, so long as we are sure that a crisis will not occur. If there seems any risk of this, we should stay with the person, perhaps sitting quietly at a desk with a book or otherwise indicating that we are not expecting more discussion but are available if the person needs to continue talking. As always, achieving separation is of major importance in the music therapist's art.[9]

The Personal Theme Tune

The personal theme has a dual role; it is a transitional object that links life within the music therapy room with life outside and a memory-jogger to promote recall of the content of the sessions. The first person for whom I ever "prescribed" a personal theme was a woman suffering from grief following a major but disenfranchised bereavement. I suggested that the song "Climb Every Mountain" might be useful in reminding her that grief can take a long time to resolve, but that if she kept battling her way to the top, she would find herself again. I drew a sketch of a rugged hillside to illustrate these ideas. My client accepted this idea and sang the song with me, with markedly good outcome before the next session.

Whatever tune is chosen, it must be familiar to the client, otherwise it cannot be recalled when the session is over. Since that first use of a personal theme, I have tried to help the client select the tune as being significant as well as familiar, but some people prefer to be given a selection from which to choose the melody that is closest to the personal need and experience. A few people have used their own parody composition, as with the woman who set her own words to Sibelius's melody from *Finlandia,* "I won't give in, I'm going to keep on trying," or a man who chose the film theme from *The Dambusters* with very similar words—"I'm going to keep on trying, *Not* let things get me down." Others prefer to use a song composed entirely by themselves, as with a patient who had been seriously depressed but who wrote about wanting the world to see her being happy. Others have chosen a known theme from a film—the melody from *Chariots of Fire* has been selected by several, and the visual associations have been helpful, the athletes running through waves to strengthen leg muscles as a theme for determination.

But any music can be chosen for a personal theme, and it does not have to be something the music therapist can play from memory on request; after the matter has been discussed, the client may bring a tape or CD of a piece of music that seems to symbolize hope, determination, or whatever is appropriate to the next session.

Final Separation

Reasons for termination may or may not be within our control:

- The client may have ceased to make progress over several sessions, and we decide on either a temporary or a permanent break.
- So much improvement has been made that ceasing therapy is seen as a positive step.
- The client is about to be discharged because this is adjudged best for his or her well-being or for other reasons.

- The patient is discharging himself "against medical advice," and we may or may not say good-bye.
- When someone has absconded or suicided, there is clearly no separation interview. Separation by suicide is an extremely painful issue for the therapist to deal with, and it is essential that we set aside time for professional debriefing and resolution.

In a planned termination of therapy, there are many points for the therapist to consider (Brodaty, 1983):

- Do we introduce the concept of separation in the previous session?
- Is it cruel to announce final separation without a chance of renewed therapy? Brodaty points out the impact on the client of having therapy brought to an end with no prospect of renewal and suggests that to give a month for further thought may help the person adjust to the mourning process of separation. This is applicable only to an extended program of work.
- Are we fostering anxiety or dependency or manipulative control by saying or suggesting that we might extend?
- Do we discuss achievements and hopes for the future but explain that it is now the client's responsibility to manage his own future and that the next session will be the last?
- Do we discuss achievements and suggest that the time for completion is close, so that the next session will probably be the last? *(This is my preferred approach.)*
- Another approach is to say that we have gone as far as we can for the time being, and the client will be able to put into practice what has been discussed and planned in the sessions. The client is free to return but not before he has given things a fair trial of how he gets on without regular therapy sessions, perhaps giving a firm time span for this return. *(I use this approach for some people.)*
- Yet another approach is to put the separation into the context of a team approach, that all treatment is being curtailed because so much progress has been made.

Whatever our approach to final separation, we must include aspects of farewell, congratulations on what has been achieved, and thanks to the client for sharing so much of himself or herself with us in that session. All of these lend themselves to expression through music, and it is appropriate to also include the person's chosen theme song which will have been used in each session of the series.

Summary

Inherent in the eclectic approach is the development of communication skills and the empathic awareness of what may be going on below the surface for any individual. This is combined with empathic skills in improvisation and in other approaches to produce an approach that is adapted to meet the needs of each individual in turn.

"One size fits all?" Never!

Chapter 4

Music Therapy for the Grief Associated with Death and Terminal Illness

Aims and learning objectives of this chapter:

- *Comprehend something of the complexity of grief associated with the end of life*
- *Come to terms with and comprehend our own attitudes toward the end of life*
- *Enhance our understanding of the many spiritual matters associated with death and dying*
- *Develop skills in the use of music to enhance pain management*
- *Extend our empathic understanding of those who grieve and of the emotions experienced by the patient and his or her significant others*
- *Enlarge our musical skills and our counseling skills to meet the needs of patients and significant others in the pre-death period*
- *Provide music therapy for the mourners after the death has taken place, when appropriate*

Grief Associated with Death and Dying

The grief associated with death and dying was the first loss situation to receive professional attention, with such ground-breaking publications as John Hinton's book *Dying* (1967) and Elisabeth Kubler Ross's many books, of which *Questions and Answers on Death and Dying* (1974) provided an initiation to concepts of grief for many people.

It is surprising to realize how innovative these writings were, how much death and dying had become taboo, with the result that stoicism had become the norm. Thanks to the writings mentioned above, and many others, we recognize today the need to grieve about death, the need to step aside from daily activities for a while to deal with separation, and to plan for the future.

We are also aware, however, of wider aspects of grieving about life events—failures, relationship breakdown, work-related disappointments, physical and emotional trauma, and other experiences. These have much in common, chief of which is the sense of powerlessness with the loss of control over one's life and circumstances, and the fear that follows powerlessness. In many traumatic or tragic circumstances, there is also a feeling of guilt—even the rape victim may think, "I should have been able to do something about it." Often there is humiliation, anger, and sadness, and if a relationship that ended in death had been ambivalent, feelings of both relief and sadness; a sudden death, with no chance to say farewell, brings its own problems.

But despite our wider understanding of grief, emotions associated with death and the prospect of death are often difficult and painful. The extent of that pain will be decided by various factors:

- The emotional investment in the relationship one had with the other
- The nature of the relationship, whether it was happy or sad, deep or superficial, positive or negative
- The nature of the circumstances: a sudden death with little or no chance to say good-bye, death preceded by sufficient time for emotional closeness, or death at the end of a long and draining illness in which communication may have eventually been silenced
- Whether the death "hooks into" other difficult experiences
- The survivor's emotional and psychological health in coping with loss and facing the future

Palliative Care

Music therapy is well accepted in palliative care, and I am fortunate in having made several visits to the Palliative Care Unit in the Royal Victoria Hospital in Montreal. The first of these visits was in 1979. I spent several weeks under the guidance of Susan Munro, whose work, supported by Professor Balfour Mount, was so influential in establishing the professionalism of music therapy for those who are dying (Munro, 1984).

One may imagine that grief resolution in palliative care is related only to death, and the dying process and to the changes and separation associated with these. But the music therapist who works in this area finds that there are other issues, arising from events and relationships from both the immediate and the distant past.[1] The work requires a broad basis of understanding, so we can provide appropriate help for patients and others as they cope with the sadness, fear, anger, and pain of the present as well as resolve past conflicts and misunderstandings.

One of the most difficult emotions that relatives face is that of relief at the prospect or the experience of death. This occurs when the relationship has been difficult and painful, but also happens to parents at the death of a child of any age who has been a source of unhappiness, distress, anxiety, exhaustion, or despair. As with so many human emotions, the feelings that are experienced occupy a spectrum, from minor relief at the prospect of undisturbed sleep when nights have been disturbed by a child's long illness, to major thankfulness when, for example, a destructive and violent relationship with an adult child is ended.

Other complex situations can arise in palliative and terminal care as the result of unresolved marital or parent-child conflict with the patient or unresolved sibling rivalry between family members. There may also be difficulties when the patient has been involved in a relationship that is seen by family members as discreditable; in such a situation we may observe rivalries between parents and the partner, and the loser in that rivalry can then suffer from disenfranchised grief (Doka, 1989).

The music therapist may or may not be able to facilitate resolution of the complexities of past and present relationships in the time remaining before death. We have to decide whether the dying person is capable of sharing in resolution or whether all we can do is support those who are left as they try to let go of the past or reach consensus about the present. Those who are dying sometimes disclose needs to ask forgiveness or express regret for past faults. Fortunately, most of the matters that need resolution are somewhere in between the extremes, and we seldom have to facilitate resolution of extreme pain from the past or relief of the present. But we can never assume that emotions observed in palliative care are related only to the dying process itself.

Our Own Attitudes

In working with those who are dying, or who perceive themselves as dying, we must look first into ourselves:

- How do we respond when we see someone for whom illness has supervened, someone for whom the best endeavors of the helping profession are seen to have "failed"?
- Do we share the sense of failure and anger that may be demonstrated by actions and words of our clients or their families? Can we empathize with those feelings?
- How much difference is there between our feelings about the death that brings to an end a long and fruitful life and the untimely death of a young person?
- How do we respond if someone wishes to speak about life hereafter? Do our own feelings and beliefs take over? Can we work comfortably with someone whose views are different from our own, or do we feel compelled to preach our own faith or our own agnosticism?
- How well do we empathize with people whose attitudes to life and death are culturally different from our own?

- If we have strong personal views on moral issues, can we stand back from these if we work with people who have syphilis, AIDS, or other disorders that might be seen as linked with those issues?

Spiritual Attitudes That Color Responses to Life and Death

For those who work with older people in long-term care, it is both sad and interesting to see how often people describe or perceive themselves as dying, not because death is near but simply because they are no longer productive. This may be part of a depressive illness, in which feelings of uselessness and being a burden to family or society lead to a wish for death and even suicide. Some important research into palliative care in Canada showed that desire for death is significantly less when depressive illness is dealt with adequately (Chochinov, Wilson, Enns, & Lander, 1994). As I have commented elsewhere (Bright, 1997b, p. 12), these findings have important implications in debating euthanasia. It is also significant that pain can be a manifestation of depression. (Knorring, Perris, Eismann, Eriksson, & Perris, 1983).

The wish for death may be a consequence of the Protestant work ethic, which taught so powerfully that work is good, that an unspoken and tragic corollary amounting to a quasi-religious belief arose that if (for whatever reason) you do not work, you are bad. A woman in her seventies, severely and multiply disabled by rheumatoid arthritis, said, "I used to help other people, but *now* look at me *(holding her twisted hands out towards me)*—I shouldn't be alive."

Sadly, a link between feelings of guilt at being unproductive and a distorted religious belief in a punitive rather than a loving God is not uncommon among older people. It can be difficult for the therapist to deal with this. J. B. Phillips's book *Your God Is Too Small* has helpful discussion of harmful images of God (1986).

The grief that arises out of an acquired disability often remains unrecognized, and the onlooker may adopt a quasi-religious Pollyanna attitude with such comments as "Ah well—plenty of people are worse off than you are!" "Self-pity never helps anyone," "At least you can still see/hear/ talk/move (or whatever)," or "You are lucky to be alive!" when the person feels far from lucky and has times of wishing that he or she were dead. While this, and the situations described in the paragraphs that follow, is not a situation in which death is near, it has much in common with extended palliative care.

There are several neurological diseases that cause inexorable deterioration, and diagnosis of these may well feel like a death sentence, even if death is still far away. An exception was the response of a woman in early middle age, recently diagnosed as having multiple sclerosis, who had experienced fluctuating disability for several years. She said that to find out there was something organically wrong with her, even something as serious as MS, came as a relief because it showed her she was, after all, *not* crazy, *not* a hypochondriac, *not* attention-seeking—these having been the messages she had been given during her years of off-and-on disability. Her thankfulness, too, had a spiritual flavor, and hymns were among the music she requested each week.

When a life-threatening or life-destroying disability has a genetic basis, parents commonly feel guilty that they have passed on the gene,[2] but siblings who escaped the gene may also experience a form of survivor guilt, such as is seen in those who survive an accident or epidemic in which others have died. One woman suffered deeply over her brother's Huntington's disease, spending enormous sums of money taking him on a fruitless quest to faith healers around the world because she felt overwhelmed with guilt that her life had gone so well and his had gone so badly. As she said, "It could've been me. It was pure chance that the gene missed me!" Dealing with philosophical rather than scientific questions about why such genetic defects happen demands much from the therapist.

In some cultures, religious tenets and beliefs strongly influence responses to adversity, and it is especially tragic when these include a belief that a neonatal death or an abnormality in the newborn is a punishment for evil behavior of the mother. The music therapist involved with a family holding such beliefs will need knowledge of the cultural and religious background of those beliefs, and it is wise to seek support from colleagues.

Spiritual attitudes to survival after death color people's responses to terminal illness. It is significant that Hinton, in his research on dying, found that those with a weak faith, who felt guilty that their lives had not been sufficiently "good," actually expressed more fear of dying than those who believed that death was the end, that there was nothing afterward (1967, p. 84).

Depending upon the therapist's own spiritual attitudes and beliefs, the music therapist will often be able to offer musical and verbal support if anxiety about pain, suffering, death, and judgment are expressed. It is also appropriate to ask for help from a hospital chaplain or other pastor who is able to relate comfortably with people who have difficulties about matters of faith.

The music requested by the patient sometimes helps us to know what is going on below the surface. The man about whom staff worried that he needed to know death was near but who seemed unaware of this asked for hymns from his childhood in an English village church choir. After they were played to him, he said, "At times like this, that's what you hang on to." This was as far as he wanted to go with conversation, but it was enough to tell us that he was indeed aware of the nearness of death and that he had spiritual confidence, something to "hang on to."

Pain Management

Ideas on pain control have changed in recent times, and it is now rare to find the attitude "We must not give you too much medication for pain in case you become dependent on it." The work of Twycross and others demonstrated that psychological responses to drugs used for pain control are different from responses to the same drugs when used for so-called "recreational" purposes and that we need not therefore withhold pain relief in conditions in which pain is a major feature (Twycross, 1980, pp. 65–92; Twycross, 1988).

But medication and relaxation techniques to dull pain do not promote total quality of life; simply being free of pain is not enough to help us feel that we are living and not merely *existing*. Quality of life in terminal illness or chronic disability involves such features as

- being treated with dignity, regarded as a real person;
- having as much information as we want about the future;[3]
- being able to make decisions about at least some life events;
- being allowed to express feelings of all kinds;
- taking part in meaningful human relationships;
- having whatever level and type of mental stimulation we prefer;
- having fun, something pleasant to look forward to!

Professional music therapy can help provide many of these.

Relaxation tapes are a popular approach to pain control, but it is important that the music on the tapes matches individual musical taste, education, and preference. (See also "How to Use Recorded Music" in this chapter.)

Preference is also the basis for selecting live music at the bedside, and the choice does not always fit the popular view of what constitutes relaxing music! In one instance, I was asked to see a young woman who had been admitted an hour beforehand to a palliative care unit, suffering extreme pain from cancer. Taking an electric keyboard, I asked whether there was any music she would like to help her feel at home in the new surroundings of the hospital unit, perhaps helps her relax and cope with her pain. (A full assessment was to be made but there was a short delay before this happened and before an appropriate pain-medication regime could be set up.) She asked for a rumba and other Latin American dances. Fortunately the keyboard had a convincing rhythm bass for several such dances, and I started to play the first dance she had asked for at a fairly robust volume and tempo in order to make it genuine. To my surprise, her eyes closed quite soon after I began, and she fell asleep; I continued to play until I was sure that she was deeply asleep.

I also noticed that her brother, who had accompanied her to the hospital and had been sitting at the other end of the room, his face showing deep anguish, had begun to cry as she relaxed and fell asleep. The nursing unit manager had looked into the room to check progress just as he started to cry; she sat down to be with him, and talk with him if he wished. I then departed.

This episode demonstrated that we cannot have set views of what music is appropriate for pain relief and relaxation—vigorous music that is familiar and well-loved may be as effective, or more effective, than quiet "wafty" relaxation items. It also demonstrated the value of empathic teamwork, in the nursing unit manager involving herself in the care of a relative as well as of the designated patient.

Practicalities

How to Approach the Patient and Family

The stereotype of the loving family grouped around the deathbed sometimes represents reality, and the music therapist here need only offer to play some music. "I'm the music therapist in this unit, and Dr. ______ suggested you might find some music helpful at this difficult time. I wonder whether there is any music your (loved one) used to like that I could play for you?"

In one instance, I found a family standing far away from the bedside. My suggestion about music "for this difficult time" helped the adult children of the dying woman first move closer to the bed and then sit on it, holding their mother's hands.

The phrase "this difficult time" is an ideal way to approach people because it is appropriate for any relationship. Saying "this *sad* time" is risky because it locks people into sadness as their only acknowledged emotion. If the relationship has been such that *relief* about impending death is the overwhelming emotion, speaking as if sadness is the normal response makes it impossible to acknowledge the truth.

One sometimes observes difficult ambivalence in relatives, when the impending death or its causes are seen as somehow discreditable; we may see this in imminent death from drug overdose, from HIV-AIDS, from alcohol-related problems, in near-death from a suicide attempt, and other situations. Again, the phrase "this difficult time" avoids judgment and may help people talk freely about their feelings, giving the possibility of achieving a measure of resolution in the pre-death period.

Reminiscence is often helpful for patient or family. A younger man, dying from cancer of the cervical spine, recorded his reminiscence about life as a gift for his daughters, with musical milestones to mark each stage of his life span. I played most of the songs to intersperse with his reminiscences, many of which were amusing, so the tape included much laughter, with short excerpts of a few actual recordings when he wanted a particular performance (e.g., "Rock Island Line" sung by Stan Frieburg—interestingly, his pain diminished while laughing about this one!). This approach can be adapted according to need.

Songwriting is helpful in palliative care, and the lyrical content of sixty-four songs written by thirty-nine patients in palliative care was usefully analyzed in 1995, demonstrating that there were seven recurring categories (O'Callaghan, 1995):

- Complimentary themes about staff, fellow patients, and friends
- Feelings for and experiences with people
- Memories of past relationships
- Existing in the future
- Expressions of adverse feelings about current life circumstances
- Descriptions of stories and nature themes
- Gratitude to family, staff, and God

Varying amounts of help and support are needed in facilitating the writing of songs by patients. Songs are also composed by therapists to support patients and their families, and this is helpful for many people (Krout, 1999).

How to Choose the Best Instrument

The instrument is chosen by the therapist on the basis of his or her own preference, skills in performance, and, most importantly, the preference of the client and suitability of the instrument for that person's capabilities. In palliative care, these instruments are useful:

- The **Autoharp,** chiefly because it provides the client with the opportunity to contribute to the music that is created, whether by sweeping a plectrum across the strings or selecting the bars to be pressed down. Some therapists use it with brilliant creativity, but others use it poorly.
- The **piano accordion** is useful because it gives a clear melody that is easily heard even by those with partial deafness, who can touch the instrument, feeling vibrations to support what is heard; player and listener are in eye contact and in close proximity, and the instrument brings back varied memories. I have been told of church services and bush dances, the accordion being used for both—but some people regard it as barely a musical instrument!
- The **electric keyboard** gives a wide range of sounds; one needs an instrument that is touch-sensitive to bring out the melody as necessary. Many patients have found it fun to press the rhythm buttons in turn and force me to change my style of playing to suit what they have selected. But some people reject it because it is not a "real" piano.
- For some younger palliative care patients, the **guitar** seems the instrument of choice, but it's not for everyone.
- Some people who are terminally ill have enjoyed playing the **lyre,** as described by Munro (1984). The vibrations are felt in the chest cavity as the patient lies supine in bed, and minimum skills and energy produce pleasing musical sounds.

Offering choice, whether of the instrument to be used or the music to be played, is important. However trivial the choice may seem, it offers some avenue of control for people living in a situation where decision making is generally lost.

One older woman, dying from upper motor neuron disease and thus functionally paralyzed, delighted to "conduct" my playing of the accordion with her hand in the early stages of the disease—but, on the day of her death, conducting with a barely perceptible movement of her index finger. The delight for her lay in controlling my playing by altering the speed at which I played. On that last day, with her husband sitting beside her, she first had me playing the "Blue Danube" waltz so slowly that no dancer could have maintained balance, then so rapidly that the dancers would have probably fallen in a heap on the floor! Although ostensibly just for laughs, this actually had profound emotional value in that, totally helpless to control her own life, she was controlling my actions.

Her husband later told me how wonderful it had been at the very end of their partnership to be able to experience the fun they had shared together through their long married life again. Despite the nearness of separation, their shared amusement had been appropriate; it did not deny their sadness in separation, but was valuable because, as so often when the terminal illness has been protracted, the time in and out of hospital had made the experience of intimacy difficult, and sharing familiar music, smiling together, helped reestablish their sense of closeness and so facilitated their leave-taking. This was no passive experience but one in which power was actively used.

How to Use Recorded Music

Recorded music is valuable in palliative care: it must be chosen by the patient so there is no risk of items being selected that are disliked by the listener, and we therefore need a large library of recorded music.

Some therapists observe a preference for New Age music in relaxation, but one cannot assume that each individual will have this preference. It may be that those who face an uncertain future find that this type of music, in which harmonic structures, modulations, and cadences are often relatively unstructured, fills their expressive needs. Others, however, (often professional musicians with a preference for classical repertoire) find it profoundly irritating.

Before suggesting relaxation tapes, therefore, one must determine musical preference and, rather than using commercially marketed tapes, it is often more helpful to devise tapes for individuals, prefaced by individualized inductions to promote relaxation or pain control. One must, however, be careful to comply with the copyright laws that apply in the country or state where the therapy is taking place.

Equipment *must* include headphones with each cassette player or CD player. As Susan Munro pointed out (personal communication, 1979) pain and panic attacks commonly occur at night, when the music therapist is absent, so it is essential that the selected music can be available to the patient at any time of day or night, without the risk of disturbing people in the vicinity. The sets I saw at each person's bedside, in the Royal Victoria Hospital in Montreal, had the buttons relabeled so that the correct control button could be pressed even by someone unable to sit up independently. Having control over at least one aspect of one's life is not the least of the benefits of recorded music!

How to Plan the Funeral

Those who know death is near may indicate that they would like to plan their funeral service. This can provide a comforting sense of control when all other avenues are lost. It is not unknown for someone to write a song to be sung at the funeral and to choose other music to be played. Sometimes this is from earlier life; sometimes it is religious in nature. A colleague told me of a woman who had done a large collage of her life story, stimulated by a particular piece of music, who asked that the music be played at the funeral and the collage placed in her coffin because it contained deeply intimate matter from her life that she wished to be kept private. Others, however, prefer to leave such creations as a legacy to family members or friends.

At one funeral I was asked to play the deceased's favorite piece, which was "Believe Me, If All Those Endearing Young Charms," which perhaps seemed inappropriate. But it was the favorite piece of his late wife, symbolizing his love for her, and therefore significant to him and to family members. For a woman who was hospitalized in Sydney when her daughter died in England and whose own health (and finances) prevented her from attending the funeral, I used the hospital chapel for a small service. The service included prayers and the favorite music of mother and daughter. It took place at the nearest time we could manage to the time of the funeral in the United Kingdom. Creativity in all forms is the hallmark of music therapy!

How to Help the Mourners

We may or may not be able to spend time with the family after death has occurred. Some music therapists have been involved in the funeral service, playing music associated with the individual.

As in the pre-death period, the neutral phrases are helpful after bereavement in facilitating disclosure of a variety of material. "As we look back over a relationship, we remember many things, don't we—some of them good and some not so good" allows people to choose their own level of intimacy and disclosure. They may or may not decide to seek formal counseling in dealing with the bereavement.

Our Own Understanding of Terminal Illness, Death, and Responses to These

Reading appropriate books gives us basic understanding of the complexities of grief. It also launches the process of becoming competent to work in the field. Some books have stood as authoritative for many years, such as those by John Hinton, Elisabeth Kubler Ross, Colin Murray Parkes, and William Worden. Others are newer and may become classics or may eventually prove to have been trendy and ephemeral. Each of us must read with an open mind and then make a decision as to which books to trust in their entirety and which to use selectively.

But we need more than books. We can benefit from participation in special training programs, which should include role play and other experiential activities as well as theoretical information. Depending upon what is available in our own locality, training may be in formal university courses leading to a master's degree, or any one of a number of less academic training programs—and some of these are more useful for a practicing music therapist because they focus less upon intellectual prowess and more upon knowing oneself and learning empathy, as students develop their own ways of relating to those in grief.

Summary

Palliative care should not be seen as limited to a named facility for terminal care, but as including all who perceive themselves as being in the final stages of living or whose relatives perceive them thus. As in all situations, therapists need to have an idea of what may be going on below the surface for client and others. We also need to understand our own feelings about death and dying, euthanasia, life after death, chronic disability, old age, "timely" and "untimely" death, and any other aspects of terminal illness that may need to be dealt with.

Above all, we need creativity—in planning and implementing sessions at the bedside or the dayroom, in songwriting on behalf of or in cooperation with the client, and in giving choices and control, whether over the music to be played or the topics to be discussed. Thus we give to our patients and clients the dignity of being allowed to make decisions, of being *people.*

Chapter 5

Music and Grief Therapy in Psychiatry

Aims and learning objectives of this chapter:

- *Develop an understanding of grief that is manifested in a psychiatric population*
- *Extend knowledge of the psychiatric disorders common to the population with whom the music therapist works*
- *Increase understanding of substance misuse as it impinges on work in psychiatry*
- *Understand the different cultural patterns that may affect people, whether they are First Peoples, migrants, political refugees, survivors of torture, or any group that has strong characteristics of behavior and belief*
- *Continue to increase self-awareness in order to deal with transference and countertransference issues*
- *Establish personal ethical and moral position when working with those whose behavior has been antisocial or criminal*
- *Develop improvisational skills in music to enhance interventions that reflect as fully as possible to the client his or her experiences, challenges, and responses, and to assist in expression of emotions, decision making by the clients, and resolution of difficulties*
- *Endeavor to extend the understanding of the role of music therapy among clinicians so that referrals and information contained in them are appropriate and teamwork is enhanced*

General Comments on the Causes and Manifestations of Grief in a Psychiatric Population

For some, the diagnosis of a psychiatric disorder is the primary source of grief because of the complex implications it carries: stigmatization; problems with relationships, employment, and study; and the loss of self-esteem that can be inherent in any of these.

Psychiatric disorder can impair one's capacity for sustained relationships or lead to rejection by those we seek to relate. It can impair one's capacity for sustained study or employment or cause adverse attitudes in our teachers or employers. Stigmatization and the effects of the actual disorders can cause any or all of these difficulties. To feel that we are "labeled" exacerbates our personal response to the initial diagnosis and our continuing experience of illness, if the condition does not respond well to treatment.

Virginia Lafond's book on the grief of mental illness is moving and helpful; what makes it especially valuable is that it is written from the viewpoint of someone who is both a professional health worker in the field of psychiatry and who herself suffers from a psychiatric disorder. It can be highly recommended for therapists, patients, and clients (1994).

We find that people with significant psychiatric disorder may have more difficulty in coping with losses than is experienced by people who are "well." Someone who is severely depressed, who perceives adverse life events as "all my fault," who thinks "I must have done something to deserve this," or who has hallucinatory voices saying, "You are useless, everyone you love will disappear, why not kill yourself?" is predisposed towards complicated grief after bereavement, relationship breakdown, or other loss.

In some instances, there is in fact a link between the illness and the event, as with the man whose schizophrenia, only partially ameliorated by medication, finally caused his wife to leave him. This in turn caused exacerbation of the negative symptoms of his illness, and the combination of all these factors led ultimately to his death by suicide.

Someone with delusional ideas of reference is likely to have extraordinary difficulty in disentangling reality from delusion when a loss occurs, as with the young woman who saw the red paint on the lampposts in the hospital garden as highly relevant to her husband's death. Those with paranoid delusions may perceive a normal death or other loss as linked with fantasies of persecution. Even without the complexities of delusional beliefs, intrusive thoughts, manic responses to loss, hallucinations, and so forth, the psychiatric patient remains highly vulnerable to sadness and confusion.

The quality of grief is affected by the probability or improbability of situations changing.

- Has the partner gone permanently, or might the partner return if medication is used regularly?
- Is there any hope of renewed employment, or is the illness such that there is no realistic hope of this?
- Is there any chance of the university giving an extension of time so that exams may be taken later?
- In some places in the world, we shall need to know whether the patient

has sufficient health insurance to cover several sessions or whether we must work as rapidly as possible.

If the referral has been adequate, we may already know the answers to these; if not, the social worker will be able to give information. But we need to bear the significance of these matters in mind as therapy proceeds.

When Is Music Therapy for Grief Resolution Appropriate?

In any major psychiatric hospital we shall meet people with any one of a variety of disorders, and the appropriateness of music therapy for grief resolution at a given time is determined partly by the severity of the disorder and partly by the client's particular needs.

Music therapy has much to offer for grief resolution for people with any diagnosis and following any loss. The decision as to *when* interventions should begin is, however, not always made easily, and normally a decision is preceded by discussion between the psychiatrist and the music therapist. If there has been a music therapy assessment, the results of this will also contribute to making decisions as to when and how music therapy should begin.

When people are acutely ill at admission with a **psychotic disorder,** especially with paranoid features, a drug-induced psychosis, or extreme suicidality, they are usually inaccessible for grief therapy through music. Any work that requires introspection or consideration of changes in relationships must wait until people are less disturbed.

Those with delusional beliefs, florid hallucinations—whether visual or auditory—and ideas and delusions of reference may remain inaccessible for some time. The disordered thoughts affect our work in music, discussion, or graphics and so make our interventions of doubtful value—perhaps useless—and sometimes harmful. There may, however, be a benefit when a patient who has not previously disclosed these beliefs discloses them to the music therapist because the nonthreatening atmosphere of our sessions allows defenses to be relaxed. This allows us to contribute to team diagnosis.

It is appropriate to use music therapy interventions in **bipolar disorder** (formerly called manic-depressive disorder), but the nature of those interventions will depend upon the severity of the disturbance, whether or not there is a pattern of rapid cycling, and whether the person is in the manic or the depressive phase when seen.

It is difficult to imagine what life is like for people with a severe bipolar disorder. There are conflicting views as to whether life is more difficult for those who have rapid or infrequent cycles of mood, and even here there is controversy as to what we mean by "rapid cycling." This was discussed in an article (Persad, Oluboka, Sharma, Mazmanian, & Kuenoman, 1996) that stated that rapid cycling can be

- continuous, with no free interlude between episodes;
- ultrarapid, the moods shifting sharply within the same day—or even the same hour;
- with two or more complete cycles in a year—without an interval between.

This last corresponds quite closely to the four episodes per year listed in *DSM-IV* as the criterion for rapid cycling bipolar disorder, but Persad and colleagues prefer the definition "a pattern of recurrence and frequency of a manic and a major depressive illness." The writers also remark that it is only in *DSM-IV* that rapid cycling bipolar disorder has been acknowledged as an entity; no such category appeared in *DSM-III-R.*

We may not need detailed theoretical knowledge about this matter, but we must try to understand how people feel about the frequency of their episodes. It is also important to realize that many people have experienced problems with mood swings for many years before their condition is diagnosed. Professor Gordon Parker, at the University of Sydney, gives the average figure of eight years of illness (with several assessments by a general practitioner and specialist psychiatrist) before a firm diagnosis is made (1999). It is therefore not surprising that some people with bipolar disorder have a deep mistrust of the helping professions and doubt the efficacy of any interventions that are offered. Because music therapy offers something different, we may escape that stigma.

Biological depression, in which episodes are experienced without any precipitating event, has similar damaging effects on life and relationships. One young mother spoke despairingly of her feelings of failure at not being there to support her little girl on the day she started kindergarten, and her guilt at what a miserable failure she was as a wife, rarely enjoying sex, often being hospitalized. The unpredictable nature of the episodes was a major feature of her despair so that it seemed depression bred depression.

In **all forms of depression,** self-esteem is extremely low, and it is difficult to build this because of the inner doubts of the client. Warm commendations for musical improvisation, for songs written, or for any other achievement are interpreted, however genuine we are in our remarks—as (spoken) "You're being kind because I'm so hopeless" or (in thought) "She's only saying that because she doesn't really know what I'm like below the surface." As in obsessive-compulsive disorder, perfectionism is the unattainable goal. One young woman, whose mother had bequeathed her a piece of jewelry as a token of love for her daughter, was told that it had been lost by a member of the family. Instead of being angry, her immediate thought was, "Oh well, I didn't deserve it anyway."

So what can the music therapist do? Simple reassurance is generally fruitless. We cannot argue people out of their self-assessment. One approach is to play deliberate and moderately unobtrusive wrong notes in a well-known piece of music (MT = music therapist and P = patient).

MT: Did you notice the mistakes?

P: Yes!

MT: So was it all right for me to go on, or should I have gone right back to the beginning?

P: Of course it was okay to go on!

MT: Did the wrong notes totally wreck the piece?

P: No, they were just a slip, not important.

MT: What about life in general—is it okay to go on even if we are not perfect?

This last, of course, is "the $64,000 question." Our challenge is to help the client make the transfer from "It's okay for the therapist to play a wrong note" to "It's okay for me to make mistakes and be imperfect." But this cognitive-behavioral approach using music has proved of lasting benefit, helping people to achieve changes in attitude over a period of time.

Patients with **borderline personality disorder** present a challenge to the music therapist as well as other professional, and are sometimes seen as the most complex people with whom we ever have to deal. One should be aware of the diagnosis, talk to colleagues, beware of manipulation and splitting (see chapter 12, "Splitting by Intent"), and try to avoid a complex relationship as much as possible, focusing on honesty rather than imagination.

One such young woman told a dramatic story of total disaster with an array of loud and vigorous histrionics, ending her "recital" (which is how it seemed) by saying "*Everything* I do goes wrong—even my *suicide* attempt was a *failure!*" As she said this, I caught her eye and, absolutely simultaneously, we both collapsed into helpless giggles. Initially I was horrified that I could be so unfeeling, but gradually realized that the relationship had suddenly become real. There are times when something comes to the rescue and what seems a professional disaster turns a relationship around for the best.

This young woman's life *had* in fact been fraught with unhappiness, but her histrionic presentation tended to obscure this. She was perceived primarily as a manipulator, difficult to work with. Our shared hilarity led to a therapeutic alliance that lasted throughout her extended admission, and interestingly, despite our initial laughter, we were able to work seriously together at a deep level through improvisation, songwriting, sketches, and other modalities. She was able to weep freely as she dealt with some of the tragedies of her life, and a good outcome was achieved.

Obsessive-compulsive disorder (OCD) has been especially challenging to me because of the difficulties experienced in facilitating creative improvisation due to the relentless search for perfection and the endless repetition that burden the sufferer. Most of us can recall having childhood rituals that brought a sense of safety, but if broken, presaged nameless doom. Such rituals included stepping in the squares of the footpath (sidewalk) and not on the lines, hitting or touching alternate uprights in a fence, and so on.

Fears of this kind terrify a child, and when they continue in adult life, as for the person with OCD, the fears sometimes seem to be delusional in nature. The person with OCD still protects his or her existence from doom by following rituals of one kind or another. One such young man played Pachelbel's Canon in D for four hours nonstop in an attempt to get it perfect.

Improvisation was initially impossible for him, first because it could never be perfect and second because in improvisation, he could not foresee what was going to happen next, epitomizing his fear of lost control. For this reason, other means had to be devised to enhance creativity within the parameters of control levels that were acceptable to him. For instance, he composed a melody while I played an Alberti bass accompaniment, in which accompanying chords are played in a broken-chord pattern sufficiently predictable for him to be able to invent a melody on the top. Songwriting was also possible for him as our sessions continued.

Gabbard comments that people with this disorder do not appear to enjoy the activity in which they endlessly engage, that they appear driven to do so (1994, p. 593). This matches my own observations of the compulsion of many different patients to repeat various behaviors with seemingly no prospect of ever achieving the required perfection and control. Some have developed substance misuse as a fruitless form of escape.

No guidelines can be laid down for such work except to build trust by initially accepting the person's needs for control through ritual, yet without pretending to need those same rituals oneself. With the young man referred to above, I found my speaking of childhood rituals helped him feel comfortable with me, however he also had to accept that I had been able to outgrow these. The "wrong note" method presented above as helpful with depression and perfectionism is also useful for OCD.

Other disorders present their own difficulties. Our best source of competence is knowledge of the disorder and knowledge of the person—whether we are working with schizophrenia, depressive illness, obsessive-compulsive disorder, or any other psychiatric problems, with dementia at one or other stage of that particular disease or combined with a psychiatric disorder.

Substance misuse: The work referred to here took place only with patients who had been admitted to a special unit for drug and alcohol rehabilitation within a psychiatric hospital. The applicability of the approaches for other populations with drug and alcohol problems is therefore uncertain, but I hope that the ideas will be of value to those music therapists who are working in the community. Some further comments will be found in chapter 9. The inclusion of the work in this chapter is justified by studies noting a high percentage of persons misusing alcohol also have a psychiatric disorder (Rounsaville, Dolinsky, Babor,

& Meyer, 1987). It is therefore probable that many such people misuse substances as a form of self-medication by drinking or using illicit drugs to keep their hallucinatory voices quiet, to dull the pain of rejection in relationship breakdown, to numb the intensity of flashbacks in post-traumatic stress disorder, and so on.

It seems clear that people with a dual diagnosis of drug or alcohol dependency and a psychiatric disorder, may be treated less well than one would hope. This can happen if the staff of the psychiatric unit say, "We cannot help him until he has dealt with his misuse problem. Come see us when this has been achieved." The staff of the substance dependency unit may respond to a request for treatment by saying, "We cannot deal with his substance abuse problems until his psychiatric disorder is dealt with successfully. Come to our substance misuse rehab unit when this has been achieved."

Although today there are an increasing number of dual diagnosis units, the person with dual diagnosis is not necessarily accepted for management and, in my observation, older people who have an alcohol problem in addition to depression, schizophrenia, or other psychotic illness (whether recent or long-established) are fortunate to get adequate and sufficient care. The psychogeriatric unit in which I have worked has recognized the challenge of dual diagnosis but this is far from universally true.

People with these problems have difficulties in resolving grief, and especially so if extended misuse of alcohol has caused frontal-lobe damage in which insight and planning skills are often impaired (Walsh, 1978, pp. 109–152). The music therapist who works in grief resolution may therefore have to depend more upon cognitive-behavioral and less on insight-orientated approaches. But insight is still possible for many whose drinking or other misuse is of more recent origin.

Vignettes to Illustrate These Points

- A person whose appearance suggested Klinefelter's syndrome,[1] described in a music therapy session how he drank in order to be accepted into the male group, which otherwise rejected him, but did not explain what he thought was the reason for this rejection. Although the matter was not discussed except by implication, he gave the impression that drinking also helped him deal with the emotional pain of his abnormality. The physician in charge of the unit wished to arrange for chromosome testing to be done, but the patient left the hospital when this idea was suggested to him.
- A young man who in childhood had been dressed in girl's clothes by his parents and then raped by his father took drugs to dull his emotional pain at memories of this cruelty and its aftereffects in his life. The interpretation of improvised music that led to the disclosure of the background to his unhappiness was particularly revealing: he interpreted some loud discordant music as two men knocking at a door, one shouting, "Let me in,

let me in," and the other shouting, "Let me out, let me out." This led to disclosure of the sexual abuse and his own gender uncertainty.

Memory can produce so many twists and turns that obscure reality, that it can be difficult to discern the precise chronology and nature of events that are described (Mollon, 1998, pp. 13–20). Many factors are involved in remembering the past, but we may be able to obtain corroborative evidence to support the given history. If there is neither delusional thinking nor leading by the therapist, disclosures that follow improvisation are probably reality-based.

There are some who claim that losses caused the substance misuse, when in fact it was the misuse that caused the loss—although such claims are not necessarily false. I have worked with people who were able to change their patterns of substance misuse when the problems that were said to have caused their substance dependency were resolved. In this situation one must assume that the history described to us *was* accurate and that the initial dependency or an increase in substance misuse *was* in fact due to the problems. (See also the vignette about Matthew under the heading "Empty-Chair Work and Other Symbolic Interventions" in this chapter.)

For others, unfortunately, we eventually realize that we have been deceived, intentionally or unintentionally, as with the man who insisted that his hazardous drinking began when his wife left him. Family interviews revealed her departure was the consequence of his heavy drinking and abusive behavior toward her when drunk.

There is enormous controversy as to the nature of alcoholism, whether it is a disease entity or a "bad habit" (Bright, 1989). Vaillant's Problem Drinking Score, PDS, which acknowledges that the hazardous use of alcohol can arise from a wide range of factors, is a useful method of scoring (Vaillant, 1983, pp. 27–30). Gabbard says we must remember that alcoholism happens to people, and he rejects the concept of a single etiology for the syndrome, saying that it would be better if we referred to "the alcoholisms" (1994, p. 362).

Vaillant also discusses cultural factors, such as the greater ready acceptance of public drunkenness in France than in Italy, and his book includes an interesting chart of alcohol misuse in different cultures (Vaillant, 1983, pp. 58–61). For international readers, however, this chart is of limited usefulness because it describes cultural factors affecting alcohol use only in people who have migrated to the United States, rather than people in their native countries, and there may well be discrepancies. The entire study is of particular interest because it was a prospective study of a large number of people, carried out over some 30 years, so the research results and the conclusions drawn carry greater weight than those of researchers whose work was entirely retrospective.

Music therapy for grief resolution is difficult and outcome may be poor when we work with clients whose memory and insight are severely impaired as a consequence of prolonged abuse of alcohol. We need to be aware of this to protect ourselves from feelings of failure as well as to make our plans realistically.

- Peter, who had severe brain damage affecting memory and insight, was unable to remember that his wife had divorced him and grieved constantly that she did not come to visit him. Although each day the staff told him as carefully as possible that there had been a divorce, he seemed unable to remember this. He was referred for music therapy to see whether this could help him remember the facts of the matter, deal with the grief of no longer being married, and the grief of knowing it was his drinking that led to the end of the relationship.

  Peter enjoyed the music sessions, which focused initially on trust-building through the music of his European homeland, and he did eventually come to realize that the marriage was over. This did not occur through the music therapy intervention because another member of staff wrote into Peter's diary that his wife had divorced him on such-and-such a date. Except for those few residents who forgot, all residents in the unit at that time carried a diary clipped to their belt loops as a substitute for memory. The diary entry about divorce had been written in an attempt to help him adjust to reality, avoiding the daily and sometimes hourly question and answer as to why his wife had not yet arrived.

  Our session on the day immediately following this diary entry, however, was one of tragic unrelenting grief and was followed the next day by a serious suicide attempt. It seemed that there was finally some imprinting of the loss on his mind. The staff debriefing and discussion that followed this event led to a deeper understanding of the needs of the clients in the unit, but it seemed that there was no clear solution to such severe impairment of memory and insight.

Cultural Issues

We must be exquisitely sensitive to cultural diversity, whatever disorder has been diagnosed. When working with an Australian Aboriginal, for example, I always ask whether the client wishes me to use his or her white-man name or the tribal name. One young man, who had been moved from his tribal home to a city foster family in early childhood, initially needed to be addressed by his tribal name. Later, as he worked through his grief about this fostering and other issues, he wished to be called by his acquired white-man name.

I also check whether Aboriginal persons have lived a tribal life, in which case eye contact with me will be taboo because I am of a different skin (similar to clan). For those who have been largely "de-culturated" in city life, their eye-contact behavior and the implications of these may well be the same as those of white people. But this is not always so. A city-dwelling psychiatric nurse of Aboriginal descent told me she had occasional difficulties with eye contact and these puzzled her. During a case review meeting, I mentioned the difficulty an Aboriginal patient had with eye contact in his ward relationships. The nurse then realized that she was still affected by her early childhood years of traditional culture.

Other music therapists who work with First Peoples will know about particular taboos and social customs in the populations they serve, and adjust their work and their interpretations of observed behavior accordingly.

Individual Work in General Psychiatry

Much of our work in music therapy is based on the belief that people need to understand the background of their own difficulties, even if all this does is to take away feelings of guilt and help them express their emotions (probably through music in some form). In such therapy, we do not merely transfer blame from one person to another, because this can lead to playing the "what do you expect from a sick man" game described by Eric Berne (1960, p. 77), in which one rejects all responsibility for behavior and relationships on the grounds that "after all the awful things people have done to me, how can I be expected to be normal?"

Instead, we help our clients understand the domino effect—although usually it is impossible to identify exactly what started the process—in which problems in one generation lead to problems in the next, and the next, and so on, unless or until the cycle is broken. This understanding helps take away disabling guilt and the angry, illogical blaming in which everything that goes wrong is ascribed entirely to others or may even become a call for revenge.

Psychiatric disorders carry a heavy burden of stigma, which causes further grief to both family and sufferer. Ideally, therefore, the end result of our interventions is an enhanced sense of mastery and reduction in feelings of stigma and powerlessness.

Approaches in Grief Resolution with Individuals

Our methods of working vary, but a few general comments are given here:

- New events "hook into" events from the past, and we often find ourselves responding on the basis of those events instead of or in addition to the present occurrences.
- Although perhaps rivaled by smells and scents, music is possibly *the* stimulus of recall and responses to any given piece are highly individual.
- Music is the treatment of choice for many grieving people to facilitate resolution of their loss.

As we know from the work of various researchers, there are what I refer to as "Gatekeepers of Recall"—past events and relationships that either facilitate or impede the accurate remembering of the past. Thus, because of the nature of the experiences, those with post-traumatic stress disorder cannot stop remembering, suffering flashbacks (Rauch et al., 1996) and other emotional pain. Both of these interfere with ordinary living, because the traumatic nature of the events prevents the brain from processing the events and laying them down in memory in the normal way (van der Kolk & van der Hart, 1991).

When we use music to elicit memories in the practice of music therapy in psychiatry, we make many therapeutic decisions based on consideration of individual need. We must never attempt to elicit a painful memory until we know the person will have support to deal with what is recalled. For some people, empty-chair work is helpful, as in the first vignette below. When painful memories are all too present, our task is to make these memories manageable, not probe ever more painfully into them. For some people with those problems, empty-chair work is also helpful, as shown in the second vignette below.

Empty-Chair Work and Other Symbolic Interventions

The general methods were described in chapter 3, and although they are inappropriate for some people with psychiatric disorders, there are some for whom the approach is useful.

This section includes two illustrative examples:

- Tom, a young man who had been hospitalized annually at the same time of year since he was 16, was able to ask forgiveness from his mother for having arrived home late from school one day to find her on the floor, dead from a major cerebral hemorrhage. He also came to realize her disability would have been so severe if he had arrived at his usual time and she been revived, that death would have been her certain choice, so his guilt could be put aside. The music she had sung to him as a small boy was the key to resolution, by regaining their earlier relationship before guilty feelings made recall impossible.
- Matthew was an experienced driver suffering from post-traumatic stress disorder and disabled by distressing constant flashbacks of the sounds, smells, and sights that followed an accident on a two-lane highway. Rounding a curve he saw an approaching car, weaving from lane to lane. Matthew desperately tried to avoid it, but was struck by the other smaller car, which then overturned, killing the driver.

  Matthew was able to ask forgiveness from the driver for being unable to prevent the accident, due to the erratic driving and narrow road, and, in turn, forgave the other driver for perhaps having been asleep at the wheel, having driven erratically, and causing the trauma to himself, acknowledging that he too had sometimes driven when he should have been off the road. Music to evoke the appropriate mood for this extended interaction was improvised to represent Matthew rounding the curve, the other car weaving from lane to lane, the sudden noise of the impact, and then the cessation of all sound. The outcome for Matthew was good—dependence on alcohol to blot out the flashbacks and other distressing symptoms ceased, and there was hope for marital reconciliation.

Flooding for Treatment of Post-Traumatic Stress Disorder

Interestingly, Matthew had previously suffered exacerbation of his stress disorder, with greatly increased use of alcohol to reduce distress, after a therapist used the once-popular implosion, or flooding, technique—repeatedly reliving all the horrors of the death. Far from achieving mastery, it had enhanced his feeling of powerlessness to avert disaster and bonded him still more strongly to the terrible memories.

The purpose of the flooding process is to gain mastery over the memory. However, in an article on sexual abuse and torture, van der Kolk states that reexperiencing the trauma of sexual abuse by flooding in fact worsens the harmful results of the trauma (van der Kolk, 1989).[2] There is a strong probability that the same is true of nonsexual trauma, and it is reported that after debriefing many persons were found to be worse than those who had not gone through this process (Solomon, Gerrity, & Muff, 1992).

Raphael and her colleagues recommend that there is a need, not only for randomized trials[3] but also for longer-term interventions with rehabilitation rather than short-term debriefing procedure (Raphael, Meldrum, & McFarlane, 1995). We cannot justifiably equate flooding with debriefing, but debriefing, in the way it is often practiced, commonly includes instructing the person to relive the trauma.[4]

It may be that by including significant and improvised music in addition to verbal processing the therapeutic processes described above were successful in ameliorating the patients' distress because their effects were similar to those of the eye movement desensitization approach. Shapiro, the originator of the method, said the name given to the reprocessing procedure was a mistake because eye movements are not essential to the approach (1998). The approach is said to permit the brain to lay down the memories in the normal way, even after the passage of time, rather than holding them permanently in the "as-if-now-box" (van der Kolk & van der Hart, 1991).

An article by van der Kolk discussing the psychobiology of post-traumatic stress disorders (1997) is helpful for all music therapists who are concerned with recovery from trauma of any kind.

We must take care, whatever approach we use, that we do not in any way promote or encourage the continuation of the total investment of the person's identity in that of "victim." Whatever we do in and through music therapy must have as its ultimate aim the resolution of the past in order for the person to move ahead.

Another Symbolic Intervention: A Lullaby for a Dead Baby

This symbolic intervention is similar to empty-chair work in that there is an opportunity for separation to whatever extent is necessary. We are not encouraging the client to forget the dead child but giving permission to say good-bye, please forgive me, and so on.

The method was described (Bright, 1999a) as helpful for someone whose illegitimate baby had been adopted at birth into an unknown family. This is usually seen today only in older people, for whom the birth of an illegitimate child was a source of family disgrace and secrecy. In these circumstances, the whereabouts of that child will probably be unknown. The method has also been used for many parents whose child died at birth, soon after, or in childhood.

Giving the opportunity for leave-taking was particularly helpful for a young woman after a stillbirth at eight months—the child having died in utero a few weeks beforehand. Her plight was especially sad because her relationship with the child's father had since ended, so she was alone in her grief, and the stillbirth was due to a genetic defect that made it impossible for her ever to give birth to a living child. She had attempted suicide.

She was encouraged to bring a photograph and footprint of the dead child. As we looked at these articles together, her tears began—when I referred to her as a mother—the first time she had been referred to as such. These tears were the beginning of self-forgiveness for what she saw as her failure in carrying a genetic defect and so having "killed" her son.

The protocol consists of the following steps:

- Discuss the wisdom of using the method with the treating psychiatrist.
- Talk at length about the circumstances of the loss with the parent.
- Ask what music would have been sung to that baby if it had lived.
- Ask the parent to imagine holding the baby.
- Play and sing the requested music.
- Allow time for tears, saying good-bye, asking forgiveness for being unable to give birth to a living child, being unable to provide care, not being able to get the right medical care to save life, and so on. Also allow time for saying thank you for the short-lived joy of the child's life, if this is appropriate.

- De-role the parent, gradually coming back to the present, allowing time for tears, further conversation, and time alone to regain equanimity before returning to the group.

Outcome for this work has without exception been good, leading to greater peace of mind and the end of ruminations, so that the child can be recalled without undue pain.

Dissociative Illness

If we work with those who have dissociative illness, we need to recognize that there are cultural implications, because in some cultures trance manifestations are regarded as not only normal but as peak religious experiences, sought after and admired (Mead & Bateson, 1962). It is interesting to note that in the section on diagnosis of dissociative trance disorder, *DSM-IV* excludes from pathological implications any manifestation of trance that occurs in the context of cultural and religious practices broadly accepted by the person's cultural subgroup (*DSM-IV*, p. 727).

There is disagreement as to whether dissociative disorder, which results in amnesia or in multiple personalities and is a disorder more common in the United States than elsewhere, should thus be regarded as culture-specific. See the discussion on dissociative disorders, especially dissociative identity disorder in *DSM-IV* (pp. 477–487).

Within the context of music therapy for grief, however, is dissociation that is often the result of childhood physical and sexual abuse (Chu & Dill, 1990). The splitting and depersonalization that occurs after abuse may or may not result in multiple personalities.

The focus on this disorder is by no means equal worldwide (Atchison & McFarlane, 1994). These authors also remind us that dissociation is found on a continuum, ranging from a trivial loss of concentration when daydreaming to a pathological failure to integrate thoughts, feelings, memories, and actions into a coherent and unified sense of consciousness.

Although the people with whom I have worked showed marked differences in behavior from day to day, or even from hour to hour, they have not been seen as having true dissociation with *alters*. To some extent they were aware of the great contrasts in their behavior.[5]

But whatever our philosophical basis, music therapists in adult and adolescent practice cannot avoid recognizing manifestations of splitting, whether this is simply a matter of compartmentalizing different aspects of the self, loss of memory due to dissociation, or the development of several distinct personae within the one individual.[6] It is helpful if we try to understand something of the mechanisms that underlie such behavior, as well as learn how to deal with it on a practical basis. When we do sense the presence of pathological manifestations of dissociation, we should also think of the possibility of undiagnosed childhood abuse, post-traumatic stress disorder, panic disorder, and eating disorders (Chu & Dill, 1990).

Vignette

Josie, in her mid-twenties, was admitted because of self-harm, slashing her arms and burning them with cigarettes. In her second music therapy session she said this was the only way she could reassure herself that she was real. She also showed other features of depersonalization and splitting of the different aspects of herself but there was no indication of full-blown splitting into separate personalities.

Josie admitted to heroin use and satanic cult involvement. She appeared disorganized and disheveled, yet after initial assessment was over she was able to improvise on a drum set while I provided a simple chord bass until she was able to work alone. Her improvisation showed organization skills that belied her other disorganized behavior.

As part of the assessment in our first session I used my large photograph of the North Australian Tropical Rain Forest,[7] asked how she felt about it, and where she would like to be. She said the picture made her feel safe for the first time in her life—she would not need to hide because it was so dark and so crowded with growth.

The quietness of the rain forest marked the beginning of a sense of peace that led to a decision to change. In a subsequent session she said she felt she needed to get back to God, which we expressed in music in an improvisation that showed a marked change of mood. Later that morning, when I had been able to contact the priest and invite him to the ward, Josie and I shared in a simple spontaneous ceremony, based upon music, in which she destroyed her satanic cult books and tapes. She made her confession to the priest, received absolution, and was anointed.

Staff who came on duty later in the day, not knowing of this powerful experience, asked, "Whatever has happened to Josie? She looks *clean.*" It would be pleasing to say that this marked the complete end of her problems, but she still felt herself being pulled two ways and the conflict was painful and confusing. She did not, however, return to the arm-slashing and other self-destructive behaviors. She continued to feel "real" without resorting to producing the evidence of pain and flowing blood.

Josie did not fit the picture of the dissociated person whose alters are mysteriously unknown to each other. In the course of music therapy interventions, the two aspects of the self were clearly visible to all of us in both behavior and physical appearance. The vignette does not provide a complete template for interventions with similar people, but may give ideas as to how we can work toward change.

Gender Ambivalence

In psychiatric hospitals we work from time to time with people who are having difficulties with gender, and we ourselves may have difficulties in relating easily with those who are either transsexual (sometimes called "transgender"), transvestite, or are working toward gender reassignment. (The term *gender reassignment* is used in Australia as preferable to *sex change* because the surgery cannot alter the chromosomes that determine the sex of an individual. It is only bodily appearance of gender that can be altered surgically.) The loss and grief in such situations may be highly complex—a mixture of regrets, fear, hopes, and ambivalence about the change. (I attended a Journal Club[8] discussion on body dysmorphic disorder at which it was suggested that for some individuals rejection of sexual organs and gender is similar to the rejection of body parts seen in body dysmorphic syndrome [Phillips, 1998].)

Gender reassignment is also complex for the therapist. Is a woman therapist comfortable if, as an indication of kindness or empathy, she briefly touches the hand or arm of a client who is dressed as a woman but who still has a male body because surgery has not yet taken place? touches someone who has had gender reassignment surgery? Might the action be misconstrued as flirtatious, even seductive, implying that for her the person is still a man? Or does the touch emphasize woman-to-woman interaction, reinforcing the belief that the surgery has been effective? And is all this something we can bring out in our sessions, or should it remain a taboo topic?

The work we do through music to help the client transcend personal difficulties may differ little from any other grief resolution, but the thought processes underlying our planning may be even more complex.

Defense Mechanisms and Adaptation

Remembering events and relationships may or may not lead to comprehension and self-understanding. Our capacity to learn from the past is much influenced by our present supportive resources, our self-esteem, and our customary coping strategies. Throughout his book on adaptation to life, Vaillant usefully describes defense mechanisms as *adaptive mechanisms.* The term is appropriate because such mechanisms can either be helpful or harmful to our way through life and vary greatly from one person to another (Vaillant, 1977, p. 80).

Interpretation of Defense Mechanisms by the Therapist

There are those whose life is so tragic that total recall is harmful. Stafford-Clark's opinions are relevant here. He reminded us that to understand reasons for problems does not always enable us to change. Knowledge alone is not enough (1963, p. 296). Although he was writing of formal psychotherapy, his remarks also apply to the many faces of music therapy.

Vaillant reminds us that, because defense mechanisms are unconscious, their interpretation is damaging unless the therapist has "the time, the love and the patience to share responsibility for the consequences." He goes on to say that "trying to reason with or discipline adaptive mechanisms is likely to prove as effective as trying to stop the wind" (Vaillant, 1977, p. 90).

Defense mechanisms have a protective value in allowing us to go on in life, even when circumstances cannot be changed. For those whose lives are so tragic that change is impossible, supportive approaches are the only appropriate therapeutic intervention. We must be aware of this as we choose the type of music to use and in discussion following the music, lest our cleverness—our wish to show how much we have understood of the reasons for behavior—does harm.

The eclectic approach is especially useful in psychiatry because it takes into account the needs of each individual, whether these are the result of the disorder itself or a life event, and it allows for the limitations that a psychiatric disorder places on the client's ability to cope. This sets us free from rigid adherence to a particular school and allows us to be more adaptable and responsive. (See chapter 3 for a summary of approaches.)

Transference in Therapy

Whether we use insight-orientated methods alone or use them in conjunction with, say, cognitive behavior and counseling approaches, we must be intensely aware of the psychodynamics of the therapeutic relationship, aware of the client's possible need for dependency, and our own response to this. We must be watchful for the effects of transference, when the client behaves as if we were someone from his past, repeating symbolically those past relationships. We must monitor our own responses to the client in countertransference or sometimes our own "primary" transference.

This process is prominent in psychiatric work, but not unique to it; anyone who has experienced difficulties in relationships can respond in the same way toward another significant person. The topic is therefore discussed in chapter 12.

Is it helpful to deal directly with transference in psychiatric music therapy for grief resolution? Therapists who use a long series of sessions can safely wait until the client recognizes the process spontaneously, but when admissions are brief we need to make a decision on this. I have never confronted the client strongly with what is going on, even though I have thought, "Hey, you're treating me like your mother, but I'm not your mother, you know!" But a low-key remark such as "It can be difficult to separate what happens in therapy from what has happened to you with other people in the past" has helped to facilitate insight. It also allows the client enough emotional space to reject or ignore the idea if he feels unable to address the issue for the time being.

Although I have never verbalized it, an awareness of the other side of the situation is certainly there. "And I am afraid you seem to remind me of someone with whom I always had difficulties, but I will try to be aware of this and not let the relationship suffer because I transfer *my* problems to you!" We must also recognize our own countertransference, the way our attitude to our clients is colored by our own needs and experiences, and by our response to the client's often pathological behavior towards us. As with transference, the response is not limited to work in insight-oriented music therapy in psychiatry; it permeates the whole professional work of the empathic therapist, no matter what our philosophical position. Ideas on countertransference have undergone considerable change in the years since Freud's original definition, and Gabbard's discussion of the matter is helpful, as are the many specific references and case histories throughout the book (1994, especially pp. 12–13, 159–160).

There are connections between gender specificity and the processes of transference and countertransference, and I have previously discussed the question as to whether a client who has difficulties with a person of a specific gender does better when working with someone of the opposite gender, or whether the work is more productive if the therapist is of the "difficult" gender so that all the problems come to the surface more obviously (Bright, 1986, pp. 184–185).

No definitive answer has emerged in the intervening years, but it is clear that "the client feeling comfortable with the therapist" is not necessarily the same as "the client making progress with difficult matters." To achieve change may necessitate challenging encounters rather than comfort! Possibly there is no one right answer. If we find ourselves "stuck" working with someone who has strong feelings about gender, it is worth both considering whether our failure to progress is linked with feelings about gender and discussing this in our professional supervision as well as in case review.

Meaning in Music

Meaning in music was discussed in chapter 2, but we must consider it again in the context of psychiatry because responses to improvised or unfamiliar music can be paradoxical, and the responses or interpretations may be linked to a psychiatric disorder.

- Improvised music was played for a psychiatrically disturbed man as well as staff members. The staff interpreted the music as symbolizing turmoil and anger, while the client described the music as being peaceful. He revealed later that the music by representing his own inner turmoil brought him peace. This explanation was logical, yet his first response, that the *music itself* was peaceful, seemed paradoxical.

- A young man, frustrated and angered to desperation by his quadriplegia, suicidal yet with no means of achieving his goal of death, heard a peaceful, unfamiliar item as representing anger and frustration, projecting his own overwhelming emotion onto the music.
- A paradoxical response is often observed in familiar music because of personal associations. The woman who wept in the midst of a group who were smiling with enjoyment on hearing an old love song felt only sadness because it reminded her of failure of love in a disastrous marriage.
- A man playing very fiercely on drums could have been assumed to be expressing anger, especially as he had recently had an illness that left him with residual disability. But he explained that his playing expressed his determination to recover from the aftereffects of his disability, and the muscular power shown in his playing was in fact a satisfying achievement! His meaning was thus very different from that which might have been inferred by the therapist.

Graphic items are also interpreted differently by individuals because of their background, culture, psychopathology, and so on. Well-known graphic tests are the Rorschach Inkblot tests and the Murray Thematic Apperception Tests. Some of the interpretations of the same pictures are at first sight astonishing, but the differences in interpretation of unknown music are no less varied. Both have their origins in the different experiences and attitudes toward life of the people who make identifications and state their perceptions. For some, these are an indication of their inner attitudes and motivation, sometimes of psychopathology.

Practicalities

Receptive improvisation, in which the listener can project onto the improvised music his own inner needs and attitudes, is helpful for the therapist. If he or she is able to understand the mechanism of projection and gain understanding of the self through projection and identification, this is useful to the client too. Note that the term *projection* is used here in its strict definition, meaning ascribing of one's own unacceptable feelings to others, as an *unconscious* process. But the interpretation of improvised music may also include disclosure of material of which one is aware but about which one is reticent.

Receptive improvisation can be introduced in whatever way seems appropriate to the client's personality and approach to life. A possible introduction:

"Music can express all kinds of feelings: happiness, sadness, pain, anger, and so on. Music that is unfamiliar helps us to listen in a different way, and some of what I'm going to play may sound quite strange or weird for you. Sometimes when we listen to unfamiliar music, quite strange thoughts or pictures come to mind. If they do, let's see if we can talk about them because they may help us understand the past and take a step further into the future. At this stage I just want you to listen, but later on we might improvise together if you decide you'd like to do that." (The invitation to share the improvisation may be given in a later session, when trust is more firmly established.)

How do we know what kind of music to play? Without entering an altered state of consciousness, we use our creative imaginations to enter into the life of the individual across the room. Through our empathic intuition, we can create music that may adequately reflect the emotions present in the person's mind at a given time—today, yesterday, last year, or the future.

This creativity is based upon four areas of knowledge, experience, and empathy:

- Wide reading and knowledge of the effects of illness and social disruptions about people's lives, coupled with information about the client's life or disclosures that have already been made
- Musical expertise in knowing how progressions, dissonance, and harmonies may reflect emotions for any given individual and for any given culture
- Empathic understanding of what is going on below the surface for the client—the implications of the person's words, vocal intonation, body language, and so on
- A capacity to transform that empathic knowledge into music that is right for the person

Vignettes

- The music used may be simple in the extreme: A young woman in her early twenties who had some skills in music was having difficulty coping with feelings of confusion following the death of her mother. She described feeling uncertain as she faced the future, but had difficulty expressing how profound this feeling was, even to herself. I also found myself wondering who was dependent upon whom in the mother-daughter relationship.

For her, a profound psychic experience followed the playing of the C major scale, in which I used conventional harmonies such as are used by many classroom singing teachers. Playing the scale with a gradual but strong crescendo, I stopped abruptly, with the right hand on the leading note and the left hand on the last inversion of the dominant seventh chord, the cadence incomplete. In the (weeping) emotional catharsis that followed, she was able to see for the first time the ramifications of her uncertainty, its depth and complexity, the possible reasons for it, and began to look toward the future. We then improvised together, initially to help her reestablish her personal control over the situation. Eventually, over several sessions this lead to a more positive feeling about herself and her capabilities. It seemed this had been possible only through the insight gained through the apparently simple initial intervention.

The use of the scale was certainly simple, but my rapid internal dialogue before deciding to use this approach was far from simple! Since that first occasion, the unfinished scale has proved extraordinarily useful for people with a musical background who are having difficulty coping with uncertainty and have enough capacity for self-examination to use the experience. While not enough in itself, the experience is so profound that growth can follow.

Interestingly, follow-up several years later showed that this incomplete scale remained a helpful memory as having symbolized the indecision of that time, the sudden insight, and thankfulness that this is now past, that a substance-free life is being maintained and studies resumed. Other music may be complex, but the complexity of the music is not necessarily linked to the complexity of the issues that emerge.

- The person described elsewhere as John (Bright, 1999b) also benefited from therapy that included enhanced insight. For him the improvised music, intended to convey ideas of sadness, disappointment, frustration, or anger, was heard only as fear. This proved to be the hitherto unrecognized but overwhelming emotion of his life at the time.

This projection of his own inner needs led to his being able to start dealing with this previously unrecognized emotion. Although for him a deep examination of psychodynamics of his relationships was seen as inappropriate, he benefited from his newfound insight into and understanding of his fears since it led to creation of coping mechanisms rather than to fruitless despair.

- Another young man, for whom insight-based work was one component of a more complex series of interactions in music therapy, had been asked to draw a road map of his life, marking both the high points of achievement (of which there were several) and the low points when he abused alcohol and his achievements were nullified. He prepared the road map, covering several sheets of paper, and brought it to our second session. I then improvised music to reflect the up-and-down progress of his life, both personally and in his employment, reflecting feelings of certainty and uncertainty.[9]

I became aware that he was becoming somewhat agitated as this improvisation proceeded, and I brought it to a close because I was unsure of the implications of this mood change and needed to find out about this. He said the agitation was not because the experience frightened him but because he had suddenly realized something about himself that he had never thought of before—that he was scared of success and his use of alcohol was actually intentional, although unrecognized by himself in any conscious way, as a defensive strategy to bring the period of success to an end.

This was in contradistinction to what he had always thought and to what people had said to him: "What a tragedy that the drinking took over again, just when things were going so well!" Sketches drawn on the whiteboard were used to illustrate his progress almost to the top, then tumbling down the steps with a burden on his back. The space on that burden was filled with words he suggested: *fear of perfection, guilt, anger,* and so on.

These insights, shared with his psychiatrist and other members of the rehabilitation team, led to work on

- his attitude to himself;
- his fears of failure if he reached preeminence in his profession;
- his feelings of guilt about success, because he did not deserve it;
- and treatment of the underlying depression that had caused those feelings.

Throughout this extended admission weekly music therapy sessions continued with shared as well as receptive improvisation, songwriting, and the use of a personal theme tune—his choice being the song "The Impossible Dream." Although the total approach included components of cognitive-behavioral approaches as well as the pharmaceutical management of depression, it was the insight (truly an "Aha!" situation) gained in the first music therapy session that set the scene for the other styles of therapeutic intervention that followed.

Nonmusical Aspects of Our Work and the Decisions We Make in the Eclectic Approach

Although music is the mainspring of work in grief counseling, there are other nonmusical factors that contribute to good outcome, and many questions we must ask ourselves. In these and other situations, verbal verification and discussion is essential.

- How far can we understand the totality of the problems for which our help is asked? Biased presentation of reality can occur in nonverbal improvised music as often as it does in verbal accounts of life events.
- If an emotion seemed to be expressed in the client's own improvisation, are we sure that our perceptions as to the nature of the emotions are correct?
- Guilt is frequently a dominant emotion for those who are depressed. Can

we recognize the symbolism of guilt through music alone? Can we distinguish it from doubt, uncertainty, and so on?

- Those with avoidant personality, extreme shyness, or feelings of shame may not be able to reveal their feelings—even in music—for fear of rejection or ridicule, and we must understand the individual's patterns of defensive behavior lest we perceive the improvised music as shallow or meaningless rather than defensive.

The Risks of Colluding or Appearing to Collude with Delusional Beliefs

In order to help people move on and not remain "stuck" in their disorders or their role as the patient, the victim, it is essential that we discuss what lies behind the emotions that are expressed, whether this is in improvisation, song writing and poetry, drawing, or other creative activity. The therapist who feels unable to deal with this situation and allows or encourages endless expression of an emotion such as anger, knowing that the underlying belief prompting the emotion is delusional, colludes with the illness.

My practice is to say, "I know you feel that this is all real, but I truly think it is like a nightmare that doesn't go away when you wake up. I hope that as medication takes effect you will come to see it all as having been an awful dream." This has always been acceptable even to a highly delusional patient because it does not put him down, it accepts that delusions seem true but maintains the position that they are part of an illness, not part of reality.

There are other reasons for misinterpreting events. Those who are acutely depressed and who have suffered breakdown in a relationship often insist that depression started because of the breakdown and support this in their improvisations. Family interviews, however, suggest that in fact it was the other way around, that the partner left because of the strain of long-term depression, of which the current episode is simply an exacerbation of a chronic condition. Is this different perspective a delusional belief, a conscious defense, a failure of memory, or an indication of the extent to which the process of remembering is influenced by our responses, emotional and otherwise, to the original event? We cannot always be certain, but we need to find out the facts if we can, since the linkage between illness and personal relationships is rarely as simple as it seems. Family, friends, and client are all equally in need of empathic support at this time.

Loss of psychic defenses is potentially dangerous, despite one-time beliefs in the value of catharsis for its own sake. Improvisation can be strongly cathartic but can lead to emotional decompensation in which the intrapsychic defenses are lost or destroyed and a psychotic episode is triggered. So we do well to think deeply before initiating a "heavy" cathartic procedure. Defense mechanisms are not necessarily pathological. We all use them to deal with crises, unhappiness, disappointment, conflict, or any other difficult experience, and they are often better described as coping strategies or adaptations.

But even the best coping strategies can become maladaptive if they are maintained when they have ceased to be appropriate. One sees this after major trauma, when rescue workers or combat troops must deny their natural responses in order to complete their tasks, but if this coping mechanism becomes permanent and the stress is never dealt with, adverse effects that may be resistant to change usually follow (see epilogue, pp. 185–187).

The Client's Insight

Here are some people who are able to recognize the elements of previous relationships and use that insight to gain deeper understanding of themselves in the therapeutic relationship. One always hopes that such insight may lead to changes in behavior so that other relationships may profit from this. But this is not always so. I have heard the comment: "I can hear myself saying these terrible things, and I know why I am doing it, but knowing doesn't seem to help me stop!" In this situation, interdisciplinary discussion helps us decide which way to go next in therapy.

One young woman, Janet, who gained sufficient insight into the transference she experienced in the therapeutic relationship for the experience to be useful, had been suicidal following the death of her mother because she felt that life without her mother was intolerable. She presented as very needy, personally fragile, yet with very real business skills that probably because of long-term dysthymia she dismissed as unimportant in her personal life.

From the first session it was clear that dependency upon staff and upon the sick role was likely to occur. The challenge to me as therapist was to strike a balance between providing warm reassurance and support on the one hand, and intellectual objectivity on the other. I risked becoming either the "good" mother figure on whom she might become dependent or the coldly distant therapist with whom no sense of alliance would develop.

Staff-room discussion on dependency elicited interesting ideas from various colleagues, including the belief of the treating psychiatrist that some people are so needy a limited dependency on the hospital unit is not necessarily bad, and that everyone needs something or someone who reassures them that they are okay (Brogan, 2001). Although we hope dependency on staff does not become pathological, it can be a kind of transitional object on the path to self-sufficiency.

The personal theme song already mentioned[10] constitutes for many clients a type of transitional object that maintains the links and content of the music therapy session to the rest of life, and for some this experience provides a sense of security over a matter of years. Probably because the theme is selected by the client and because it is the responsibility of the client to recall the theme in times of need, there appears to be no diminution of self-reliance. But the only music Janet loved and could recall was that associated with her mother to what seemed a pathological extent, so using a personal theme would not have been helpful.

With all this in mind, work with the patient continued on a weekly basis for a total of six sessions, during which there was opportunity for Janet to disclose in words and music her feelings of worthlessness in no longer being a loving and supportive daughter, anger with her mother for dying, and wishes for death to be with her mother. As time passed, however, the atmosphere gradually changed to a more positive approach to the future. Appropriate medication had contributed much to this, but the music therapy was also seen as very important in her progress.

Songwriting can be an indicator of therapeutic progress. Janet was able to see how she had been initially dependent on my approval and although it seemed probable that she would always be a dependent type of person, she was able to start accepting her own personal worth. She composed both words and melody of a short song that symbolized her hopes for happiness and the fact that this would allow the world to see her as a real person.

The song Janet sang and played on the keyboard was written down by me, transferred to computer, and a hard copy given to her in time for her discharge home under the care of the community mental health team. The patient herself was angry about this discharge, and I believe there was an echo here of her anger with her mother for dying, and anger with that perceived rejection. But the team's view was that the longer she stayed hospitalized the more dependent she would become and the less able to live independently. This was explained to her in a suitable manner. Outcome has been good, and it seemed probable that the song she had composed would become her transitional object to link life at home with achievements in music therapy.

In my view, songs composed by the client, however simplistic or musically ungrammatical these may be, are far more valuable than the songs we compose for our clients. Exceptions are needed when working with people who have such a level of depression or a dementing illness or other brain impairment that their creativity has been so impaired they cannot do anything more than give the final note for a cadence. But a song composed by the therapist can also be perceived as a gift to the client and this may have great value.

Some people do not have enough confidence to write a song completely independently, and it is often useful to work together on the task. One such cooperative song was composed for anger management when working with Bob, who had a "short fuse" because of alcohol abuse—that is to say, it took very little to elicit an outburst of anger. He also had problems misinterpreting what was said to him, exploding into physical violence before he had checked out what the other person really meant.

Bob suggested the themes and the type of music he wished to have—a song to help him stay cool when on the verge of exploding into rage, written in a jazz mode. I tried various phrases before we decided which form the song should take. The song was short and harmonically simple. It was easy for him to remember and sing to himself as often as possible, so it would stay with him even in times of crisis. It seemed probable that the same song would be effective for others in similar situations and the words could be adapted to meet different needs.

Hold it, am I getting it wrong?
Hold it, is there some other way?
Hold it, do I have to explode?
I'll keep my cool! ... I'll keep my cool! ... I'll KEEP—MY—COOL!

Summary

Insight can bring pain as we realize how our own behavior may have led to difficulties. It can bring reassurance as we realize that things are not always our own fault but may have arisen as part of a domino-effect series of difficulties. Insight can sometimes lead to comprehension and possible change as we relive earlier relationships through transference to the therapist and begin to understand these. But I do not believe we can expect this gradual comprehension to occur readily in the brief periods of therapy to which most of us are limited today. We may be able to promote insight and resolution by open discussion, by bringing into the open the possibility of transference and ways of dealing with this. However, there are some for whom this is inappropriate, because due to the severity of a psychiatric disorder no resolution will ever be possible, and for such people the supportive approach is required, ethically and practically.

As music therapists working toward grief resolution with someone suffering from a psychiatric disorder we will benefit from being prepared:

- We need good background knowledge of the client's clinical history; educational, social, and spiritual background; and, if possible, information about musical preference and experience.
- We need good communication with other clinicians, especially the referring professional, not merely for information, but so our work contributes to the overall management and is perceived as such.
- We have to recognize the enormous diversity of psychiatric disorders we meet, not trying to become a psychiatrist but understanding sufficiently to make our work with individuals and our contribution to clinical teamwork more useful.
- We need skills in improvising music—both reflective and shared; skills in facilitating songwriting both for individuals and groups, and the ability to link improvised or familiar music with graphic or other symbolic work.
- We need a wide and appropriate repertoire to meet the needs of clients. This may range from Palestrina to the latest pop group via Beethoven, Johann Strauss, Hoagy Carmichael, Lerner & Lowe, and many others.
- We probably also need computer skills, whether for keeping clinical records, writing articles, or composition.

If we can achieve these and have the personal stamina to do the work, life will always be interesting for us and probably beneficial to our clients!

Chapter 6

Music Therapy in Psychiatry
Work with Forensic Patients

Aims and learning objectives of this chapter:

- *Understand the factors that lead to antisocial behavior in adult life*
- *Cope with our own personal responses to behavior that is destructive or criminal*
- *Cope with being in a therapeutic relationship with a person or persons whose ethical and moral standards may differ widely from our own, but without being personally overwhelmed or changed by the experience*
- *Be able to plan programs that are appropriate to work with people whose behavior may be unpredictable and hard to understand*
- *Develop special understanding and skills in music therapy for forensic patients who have committed crimes of violence as a consequence of delusional illness*

Group Work with Forensic Patients in a State Hospital

The group work described is not directly related to grief resolution. By enhancing self-esteem and building awareness of the rights and needs of others, we increase the chances of participants changing their style of living in parallel with changes achieved through medication. This may well include coming to terms with the ethical implications of violence.

The group work took place at different times in the maximum security units of two state hospitals with men who had been found "not guilty on the grounds of mental illness," or who had been in prison before their psychiatric disorder was diagnosed. After diagnosis they were moved to a special psychiatric unit.

In the earlier days of the work, before more appropriate treatment modalities were established, the group included one or two people not classed as "PUD" (Prisoner Under Detention) who required high levels of security because of multiple suicide attempts. This last placement later ceased when more suitable intensive care units were established.

Many of the men were deemed dangerous. I was attacked on only two occasions, despite my running the group on my own in the ward. Nursing staff was on call but not physically present, and neither of the attacks carried major risks to my life or safety.

There is a percentage of persons in corrective establishments or in hospital forensic psychiatric units who are mentally retarded (Kaplan & Sadock, 1985, chap. 51). They may or may not fit into the work planned for other clients, and we need to be aware of their special needs. Kaplan and Sadock also discuss the fact that people who were acquitted on grounds of mental retardation, who in times past would have been placed in what were then seen as appropriate institutions, are now living in the community. Music therapists who work in community settings may need to adjust their approaches for such clients, taking their cognitive and other deficits into account.

Books by Murray Cox are strongly recommended for all therapists who work in forensic units in either prisons or hospitals. Cox, a psychiatrist at Broadmoor, an English institution "for the criminally insane," has written movingly and helpfully of his work, the challenges of relationships, and the innovative approaches he took in his work, such as arranging for a performance in Broadmoor of Shakespeare's *Hamlet.* (These books are listed in the bibliography.)

Free Choice and Exchange of Ideas

In one group, over many months in which there was a core subgroup of long-term participants, I observed the benefits to the participants of peer-group pressure in enhancing self-discipline and in accepting differing views of others in a request program. In this session, new arrivals used to grumble and rebel when music they personally disliked was played for the group, but pressure was quickly exerted by the group through such remarks as "*Shut up* and listen to the music; your turn will come," and "This is someone *else's* favorite!"

Nursing staff found that there was some transfer of training so that mutual tolerance was enhanced generally, and not merely in the music therapy session. In some of these sessions, each person was invited to talk about his choice and explain briefly why he had chosen that item. This assisted in verbalizing feelings and again helped in acceptance of the views of others, behavior usually *not* prevalent in the lives of criminals who are psychiatrically disordered.

There were difficulties at times. One man (in the 1970s) asked for the song about the banks of the Ohio, and after it was played for him revealed that the actions in the song matched his own, in killing his girlfriend and burying her body. Keeping one's cool and making an appropriate response is difficult under such circumstances!

Other sessions involved talking about the lives of composers, such as discussions on alcoholism after talking about Stephen Foster and singing some of his songs. In times past, when homosexuality was still not openly discussed, the life of Tchaikovsky provided a comfortable link to open conversation and exchange of views, which was helpful for those whose sexual orientation and preference was homosexual.

Planning

When one is preparing programs for this population, sessions may focus on items brought by participants when they have access to their favorite cassettes or CDs. Discussion may follow the same plan as that described in the section on general psychiatry, giving opportunity for discussion—although, if the atmosphere is volatile it may be wise to avoid opportunities for confrontation and concentrate on positive comments or simple remarks about preference.

But we do need to think out what to do if someone brings music representing satanic practices, suicide, or murder. It is helpful to discuss this at a staff meeting. Research suggests that there is no clear indication that suicide and murder are caused by such music. It seems that those who are already suicidal or violent may develop a preference for "heavy metal" music because it expresses their own feelings (Stack, Gundlach, & Reeves, 1994). We may therefore see the discussion of heavy metal music helpful as revealing the feelings and intentions of those whose preference it is, but *without* allowing the music to hype people up to the stage at which violence and death are perceived as attractive, or as the only answer to life's difficulties. Nor should we allow so much time to be used with this type of music that the preferences of others are ignored.

It is usual for music therapy groups to last one hour or a little less, but we are wise to have additional plans so that the program can be changed to something bland and neutral if the atmosphere becomes too highly emotionally charged as a result of items brought by participants or any other part of the program. In general it seems to work better if the bring-your-favorites section is but one component of a longer session, rather than occupying the whole time, so that it is easy to bring a change of feeling by moving on to the next item.

Sketches drawn on a whiteboard or pictures brought to the group and passed around may also be used for group work. One can ask the group to choose which one matches the mood of the music to be played.

One day the consultant psychiatrist suggested the group bring their favorite tapes and ask me to play them. The response from one patient was revealing: "We can play tapes at any time, but when Ruth plays the music on the piano, we know she is doing it just for us." The psychiatrist thus realized the importance of personally presented music rather than records or tapes.

Nevertheless, a program of recorded music can be useful if each member of the group brings a favorite and talks about why it is important. As with other persons in a psychiatric hospital unit, such work may support private disclosure or may touch only the borders of grief, although it is obvious that grief lies below the surface for many:

- Abandonment by parents, either in childhood or as the result of incarceration
- Fear of the future
- Fear of other patients and their behavior
- Loss of livelihood (A man with a high reputation as a poet, not a prisoner, whose work was published in many books, spoke of his schizophrenia and the need for protective care within the hospital, but spoke despairingly of his grief at not being able to write any more.)

Songwriting in forensic work, individually or in the group, is useful as described in chapter 5. For those with limited educational achievements, who may be illiterate or cognitively impaired, parody provides a good start. The choice of songs will depend on the particular situation and the creativity of the music therapist. Some possible risks of this have already been mentioned, and they require more thought when we are working with people for whom violence, anger, and delusional beliefs may be predominant.

There are links between grief and anger. If we foster a group expression of anger, are we at risk of inciting to violence? On the other hand if we prevent group expression of hostility and sadness about living conditions or other matters, are we being therapists? Is it probable that unstructured improvisation will do harm by eliciting emotions for which, in the circumstances, no resolution is possible? Individual work does not carry the same risk, because we can facilitate resolution or appropriate expression of emotions in a contained environment, but group work is probably more hazardous. This is something to be discussed openly with colleagues.

Playing instruments in a forensic group requires thought:

- Will it be reminiscent of classroom music of childhood? Many people had poor experiences in education, either because of their social background, their burgeoning psychiatric disorders, or their own very limited intellectual capabilities, and they longed to pass into the "real world" of adult life. Music lessons may have been one of the activities that were hated.
- Do we have financial or other resources to obtain expensive instruments that will be totally unlike those used by children?
- Is it likely that some participants will use these as weapons to harm each other? We know that grief and anger can be associated. If the use of percussion instruments to express difficult feelings escalates angry components of those feelings to the point of explosion, shall we be able to deal with the outcome?

If the answer to the first question is no and that to the second one is yes, then instrumental music has much to recommend it—whether as accompaniment to known items or as a development growing out of creativity, in improvisation. But if the next two questions are answered with yes, we must think again about group instrumental work, discuss potential referrals with colleagues, and (probably) settle for small-group work with some referred patients using improvisation only in one-to-one work for the others.

A music program in Sydney, part of a range of interventions by the Sydney City Mission for "Street Kids," worked well in cooperation with the music industry. Although not formally incarcerated or classified as forensic clients, many of the street-dwellers had drug and or psychiatric problems, and many had been in trouble with police and had a police record. All grieved over their lives. Many had been abandoned by parents at an early age and turned to the sex industry for money, and most of them saw their existence as "dead end," often literally.

The young people committed themselves to attending a formal studio each day at a given time for a period of several weeks, the requirement being that they should be punctual and reliable in their attendance and affected neither by illicit drugs or alcohol. They worked together to write their own songs. These were sung with a backing group of participants who were instrumentalists and recorded on cassettes and CDs—copies of which were sold.

Some of the young people subsequently gained employment in the music industry. The psychologist who ran the program was able to observe the enhanced self-esteem, self-discipline, and insight of a significant proportion of the participants, with the hope that their raised self-esteem would have lasting effects on their lives.

Depending on the ethos of any individual group, some of the songs were indeed filled with ideas of violence and despair, and as a condition of their public sale, some of the recordings had to be labeled with the required warning about offensive language. But the group facilitator was able to prevent any deleterious outcome of this and believed that being given permission to express anger with society, and to have their words and music published, had a helpful cathartic rather than an escalating effect. This work was not about grief therapy as such but, in that it helped the young people deal with the griefs that were linked with their street life, it provided a way through the grief and loss to a more normal way of living.

Suicide

As in general psychiatry, the music therapist may be asked to contribute to debriefing of staff or patients if a suicide takes place on the ward. The general approach is that described in the previous chapter. The responses, however, may be somewhat different.

Stephen, one of those who attacked me and on another occasion threatened me, had been seen as a danger to everyone in the ward. Each one of us had been threatened or physically attacked on one of his "bad days." Yet on his good days he was a delightful and productive member of the group. When Stephen hanged himself, we all experienced mixed feelings. By chance, the music group took place on the day following the death, and it was heartwarming that we were all able to exchange our feelings quite freely, acknowledging that we felt safer without him but also regretted that he had killed himself.

In the past Stephen had often asked for the song "Little Brown Jug," although he did not ever disclose why it was his favorite. So we decided unanimously that we would sing this in his memory. It was an unusual, perhaps funny, mourning ritual, but one that brought a sense of completion to all concerned.

Individual Work with Forensic Patients

As with other populations, group work normally includes case finding, so that individual work may grow from our observations of the group. In the forensic group described earlier in the chapter, individual work was undertaken with a few patients. (For comments on setting up the room for individual work with people who may have outbursts of violence, see chapter 1.)

Vignette: A Man Identified in the Group As Being at Need

Robert, a young man convicted of many incidents of arson, was a group participant, and it became clear from a number of comments he made in the group that he required personal support in the privacy of one-to-one work. He told me of his life with his mother, whose husband (Robert's father) had left home because she was an alcoholic. He described the effects on himself of his brothers also leaving home, so that he accepted responsibility for his mother from a relatively early age.

Although he had no insight into the possible connection between his life experiences and his fire setting, the opportunities for private conversation were of value. He had to remain hospitalized for many years because of hazards to society and subsequently to himself, since several attempts at self-immolation occurred later in life. His favorite songs, and the fact that I remembered them, were important to him, and later he would boast to newcomers of how many years we had known each other, although without naming the unit in which we had previously met!

Four Vignettes: Forensic Patients Referred Only for Individual Work

- **Changed attitudes.** A young man, suffering from extreme delusional illness, was referred for music therapy for grief resolution when antipsychotic medication had given him tragic insight into the nature of his crime. He described his astonishment when, after killing a close relative because he believed this was necessary to save the world from Satan, nobody congratulated him. He said this astonishment had lasted almost a year until it was replaced by horror, guilt, and remorse, as medication and other treatment took effect. We were able to talk about this as well as discuss his grief over the understandable difficulties with other family members.

Through the use of reflective improvised music to symbolize the depths of sadness, I was able to lead into a principle of counseling that has been developed for use with those who have committed horrendous crimes as a consequence of psychiatric disorder. By emphasizing the enormous sadness of knowing that an illness has led to death for someone else, it was possible to achieve a balance between the two extreme points of view that can be summarized thus:

"It was only your illness, so why feel guilty?"

and

"What a terrible thing to have done—how can you bear to go on living?"

The emphasis on *sadness* as the consequences of his actions allowed him (as it has many others) to grieve without being burdened with guilt to the point of suicide. Yet it did not deny the reality of the tragedy for the family. In using this approach, we also avoid any possibility that empathy is mistaken for collusion. These points are of enormous importance for work in such a tragic circumstance.

He later wrote a song about hope for the future using the analogy of storm clouds breaking to reveal the blue sky and sun beyond. Follow-up over the next two years showed that although his mental health continued to be uncertain, the recollection of work in music therapy continued to support him.

- **Partial resolution.** Some changes in sadness were achieved with a man who had killed his mother as a result of delusional beliefs. Empty-chair work was inappropriate for him, but through hearing the music she used to sing to him, including "Little Man, You've Had a Busy Day," he recalled that she forgave his psychotic behavior several times when he became fed up with medication and his mental health deteriorated. By remembering this, he came to believe that her love for him was such that she would have forgiven even her own death. This step brought him some measure of inner peace, his suicidality diminished, and although he continued to have times of introspection and sadness, these were less disabling than in the past.

- **Poor outcome.** There are some whose delusional illness is unresponsive to medication and whose delusions therefore remain. Jenny, a forensic client who normally lived "under license" in protected accommodation, said during one of her episodes of exacerbated psychosis, "I am glad I tried to kill my parents because it was all their fault that I am ill and in hospital." Music therapy sessions for her did not lead to any insight, but she was able at various times to express sadness, rather than anger, about being hospitalized. She gained self-esteem through learning to play simple pieces on the piano as well as composing some songs that showed her lyrical soprano voice.
- **Partial success.** Inability to achieve insight and resolution can also arise from brain impairment, but music therapy can still help. A forensic patient in his late thirties, suffering from severe bipolar disorder, had attempted to kill himself by gunshot to the head and remained insightless. This was in part at least because of the damage caused to his frontal lobes by the gunshot wound. He continued to blame the victim of his criminal acts for having provoked them, and improvisation (both receptive and shared) and songwriting made only a very little difference. He did on one occasion say, "Poor girl, she did cop it, didn't she?" and this was the nearest he ever came to understanding and sadness.

Interestingly, he looked forward to our weekly sessions, even though there was nothing of the "There, there, you poor thing" about them. We related on a fairly intellectual plane, although I was able to empathize with him to some extent over the difficulties he had in understanding the need to be under constant supervision. In an inexplicable way, he was aware that he was angry because there was something missing, although because of the brain damage, he could not define what this something was.

We discussed modern poetry and shared in keyboard improvisation, and he wrote poems and words for songs. But I also challenged him strongly about his difficult and abusive behavior with nursing staff, pointing out that their nighttime rounds were an official part of their duty and not done by choice in order to annoy him. He allowed me to do this without becoming angry or aggressive.

The clinical psychologist and I adopted a cognitive-behavioral approach in efforts to help him modify his behavior, because if he continued to act aggressively and overbearingly to staff and fellow patients his discharge to protected accommodation was unlikely to occur. The outcome was moderately acceptable to him in that legal decisions were made so that he was able to leave the hospital, although I learned from the community health team that he continued to rage at the continuing legal requirement for supervision.

Refusing a Referral

One of the few referrals I have ever refused was for a forensic patient who falsely believed that his mother had killed his father, and the patient had therefore attempted to strangle her. It was suggested by one of the nursing staff that, because my age was similar to his mother's age, it could be useful for him to work through some of this by means of transference to me. I was not willing to have individual sessions alone with the young man unless a member of staff was there also.[1] But in any case I considered it unrealistic to expect that music therapy would lead to his changing his ideas about his mother because the belief appeared to be of a delusional nature and, as his illness had so far been resistant to treatment, there was minimal possibility for insight and consequent change.

Contraindication for Empty-Chair Work in Forensic Psychiatry

Mention was made in chapter 3 on the presence of psychotic beliefs as indicating that empty-chair work should not be used. Difficult decisions may need to be made in forensic work when someone has committed a crime as the outcome of psychotic delusional beliefs and medication has dealt with the psychosis and removed the delusions but brought remorse and grief as well. It may seem a useful idea to employ empty-chair dialogue to allow the client to ask forgiveness from the person so killed, but my own decision in each and every case has been that there is too much risk of rekindling the delusional illness to allow the ethical use of this powerful approach.

Instead I have supported the patient, if this is appropriate, in thinking of the dead person and in helping him or her say if so desired, "I wish I could ask forgiveness for what I did," and then talking about spiritual attitudes to life after death.[2] It is, of course, essential to avoid making any comment that could be construed as a suggestion to commit suicide in order to talk with the deceased. On a few occasions, when working with someone whose religious beliefs make this appropriate, I have said, "I believe that God can take messages for us!" and this has brought comfort.

The ethics of such work are extensive, and sometimes one wonders about the ethics of using medication that removes delusions but allows such deep remorse that suicide attempts are not unknown. But, however attractive empty-chair work may appear as providing a lasting solution, I believe it is inappropriate for the music therapist to initiate this intervention.

Helping People to Cope—Ourselves and Others

To deal with our personal responses to the horrifying life experiences we encounter is not easy. We have to recognize the diversity of destructive and criminal activities that we may meet in forensic work as well as in general psychiatry and come to terms with our own moral stance. It is important that we do not compromise our own standards but stand back from these in order to facilitate change.

In dealing with tragic people who are their own worst enemy or whose experiences of abuse, exploitation, illness, and unhappiness contributed to the development of personally destructive or criminal behavior, we must avoid seeing them as tragic heroes. This is difficult ethically, but we should never condone, or seem to condone, criminal behavior simply because we can see how it all began and understand how far our clients are the victims of other people's pathology (Glaser, 1998).

As already mentioned, emphasis on sadness of the events is often the only solution to this seemingly insoluble problem, together with comments that assume that the person wishes to change. This process helps us deal with our own feelings about the lives of our clients, as we empathize with them in their original position of victims, and with the present victims of their present behavior. None of us fills all these requirements all the time, but if we can begin to do so, we shall find work more productive, probably less exhausting, and more rewarding.

Chapter 7

Music Therapy for Grief Resolution for Those Who Have Suffered Sexual Abuse

Note: It was difficult to decide whether to include thoughts on music therapy for the aftereffects of sexual abuse in the chapter on psychiatry or as a separate section. The decision was made that, although sexual abuse frequently causes psychopathology in adult life for a significant number of people (Bryer et al., 1987) and may also be the cause for incarceration, this is not universal; the topic was therefore given a separate chapter. But there is much overlap between the topics, so there are several see *and* see also *references.*

Aims and learning objectives of this chapter:

- *Gain skills in working with the victims of sexual abuse and responding when sexual abuse emerges as a causative factor in other problems*
- *Increase knowledge of the possible aftereffects of sexual abuse in adult life and find practical ways of dealing with these effects*
- *Determine the boundaries of therapeutic work in order to avoid eliciting false memories, to avoid encouraging the client adopting the life role of "victim," and to avoid the client becoming so deeply embroiled in the traumatic memories that emerge that it becomes impossible to move ahead*
- *Recognize that there are many different responses, including anger with the perpetrator, anger with the parent who failed to protect the child victim, low self-esteem and guilty feelings from the perpetrator's destructive verbal and physical behavior, and others*

Theoretical Background

Sexual abuse takes many forms. Abuse in childhood takes center stage at present. But music therapists may become aware of more recent difficulties, often combined with domestic violence, and we hear of it not only from the victim, but on rare occasions from a perpetrator who is horrified to be following the same behavior patterns as those personally experienced.

We cannot assume that we need to address issues of sexual and other childhood abuse only when this was mentioned in the referral. Such abuse, whether consciously remembered or not, whether in childhood or in adult life, has many destructive sequelae and has been found in the history of people suffering from a diversity of problems:

- Alcohol and other substance abuse (Mullen, Martin, & Anderson, 1993)
- Suicidality, psychiatric disorders, and admissions to psychiatric units (Mullen, Martin, Anderson, Romans, & Herbison, 1993)
- Borderline personality disorder (Mullen et al., 1993)
- Eating disorders (Palmer, Oppenheimer, Dignon, Chaloner, & Howells, 1990)
- Dissociative disorders (Lewis, Yeager, Swica, Pincus, & Lewis, 1997; Chu & Dill, 1991)
- Difficulties in personal relationships, mistrust, hostility, and other problems (Stone, 1989)

I have worked with several young women sex workers, admitted to hospital as the result of depressive illness, suicidality, substance abuse, and other problems, who have reported childhood sexual abuse (CSA), and who themselves perceive a causal link not only with their illness but also with their chosen means of earning money. One such patient said, "When sex as part of *love* has been wrecked for you in childhood, you might as well use it to earn money. It's just your body doing it, not you." This comment strongly suggested a degree of dissociation. She then drew up her skirt to show me, indelibly tattooed on her thigh, the words *Property of (name of the brothel).*

It is known that there are cultures in which sexual relationships between family members are not regarded as pathological and the people who have been involved in such accepting relationships do not necessarily suffer the aftereffects that we associate with sexuality as abuse. Is it possible that moving to another culture, in which such relationships are unacceptable and illegal, could result in a retrospective sense of damage?

In our work in Western society it is generally true, however, that sexual relationships between family members are culturally perceived as abnormal. Further, we need to understand that childhood abuse that leads to subsequent adult psychopathology has usually occurred in the context of a dysfunctional family or home in which the child has suffered many emotional traumas in addition to the sexual abuse. Childhood sexual abuse is not randomly distributed throughout the population. Therefore psychopathology in adult life is probably the outcome of multiple stressors, and not the outcome of sexual abuse alone

(Mullen et al., 1993). The consequences of sexual abuse are comparable with post-traumatic stress disorder, and it has been noted that dissociation occurs as part of post-stress responses (Erikson & Lundin, 1996). It is therefore not surprising that dissociative disorders occur in sexual abuse also.

It is important to realize that sexual abuse can take different forms and that the extent of the aftereffects depends in part upon the nature and frequency of the abuse. The abuse may consist of

- inappropriate fondling without genital stimulation;
- genital stimulation in masturbation, whether to the child, demanded of the child, or both;
- intromission (vaginal, oral, or anal).

It is known that abuse involving genital contact or intromission has more serious consequences for adult mental health than lesser forms of abuse (Mullen, Martin, Anderson, Romans, & Herbison, 1993). One may assume that the overpowering use of force and the consequent pain and frequent injury experienced by the child are contributing factors.

The attitude of the child to that abuse also varies, so that fondling and masturbation may be remembered with pleasure and only viewed with horror if and when adult knowledge brings revulsion. One finds that some women experience such shame at their remembered childish pleasure that this in itself appears to be a source of pathology. An older woman reported difficulties in relationships with men throughout her adult life and, in the course of music therapy with improvisation and counseling, realized that it was her ambivalence about teenage memories that had led to the approach-avoidance behavior.

Therapists of various professions have found it helpful to undergo training in the use of desensitization to trauma through rapid eye movement—Eye Movement Desensitization Reprocessing (EMDR). It seems there is a parallel in the reorganization of mental images between this approach and the customary rapid eye movement phase of sleep, in which the mind deals with life events. The nomenclature reflects the acknowledged importance of reprocessing traumatic memories within the structure of the brain (Shapiro, 1998; MacCulloch, 1999).

Work with Older People

It is unsafe to assume that older people will have dealt with memories of sexual abuse. We find these painful events and their aftermath can still influence the life and mental health of older people, as with the woman in her late seventies, suffering from a depressive illness with anxiety. In individual music therapy sessions for life review, she described her ongoing nightmares, and from the content of the nightmares it seemed highly probable that they had their origin in the traumatic childhood oral sexual abuse that she described.

The Tragedy of Polarization on Recovered Memories

The possible recall in adult life of memories of childhood sexual abuse, sometimes spontaneous and sometimes recovered as a consequence of therapy, is not only a highly contentious issue, but the polarization of opinion is in itself a possible source of tragedy:

- Those who really were abused are afraid to speak in case they are not believed.
- Therapists who suspect that a patient has been sexually abused dare not pursue this direction in therapy for fear that if they uncover incest and this leads to accusations by the abused person, this may lead to litigation against the therapist by the person who is accused (Mollon, 1998, pp. 6–7).
- Those who are falsely accused face ruin of their personal lives.
- Although I have no evidence that this occurs, it would be possible for abusers to shelter behind the false-memories publicity, thus avoiding the consequences of their actions and, more important, avoiding treatment that could help them change.

Avoidance could also arise from the therapist's fear that a fantasy-prone client may be led down difficult paths of false memories. Therefore the music therapist may, for one reason or another, make a decision to allow the topic to remain "off the agenda."

But can we conscientiously do this? It seems better to take these steps:

- Equip ourselves with basic knowledge about CSA.
- Understand our own attitudes to sexual relationships and gender bias.
- Take steps to monitor our own work so that we neither lead clients to false memories, nor prevent them from disclosing genuine trauma.
- Ensure that if CSA is found to be an issue in a client's life we have professional supervision from someone who is known to be trained and personally objective in such matters.
- Have a resource available in case legal advice proves to be necessary.
- Be willing, but not overanxious, to hand over to another professional who specializes in the field if we find ourselves unable to cope with what transpires.

The Nature of Memory and Its Relevance to Therapy for Sexual Abuse

Although the music therapist probably wishes to avoid being embroiled in the recovered versus false memories conflict, we must understand the background to the dispute, and so must consider the nature of memory. (In any case, it is useful to understand something of the mechanisms of memory for any population, since remembered events and relationships of all kinds are integral to much of music therapy for grief resolution.)

Steps in the remembering process may be summarized thus:

- We see something happen, read a book, or have a conversation.
- We lay down the memory of that happening as we perceive it at the time.
- We then store it in our brains.
- Some time later we retrieve the memory when we need to do so.

There is much scientific investigation about where the difficulty lies in unreliability of memory (e.g., in dementia or alcohol-related brain damage). The possibilities are

- in the initial observation and perception of the event;
- in the laying down of the memory in the brain;
- in the ability to store the memory;
- or, ultimately, in the retrieval.

None of these is a conscious matter except for the original perception. My view is that many of us who find we have forgotten something (such as a person's name at a party), never really registered the information in the first place!

Bartlett was a psychologist, working in the University of Cambridge, United Kingdom, who wished to discover more about the nature of memory and the extent to which our recall is influenced by our original perceptions of the matter to be recalled. He wished to investigate the validity of Ebbinghaus's earlier work on recall of nonsense syllables (Zangwill, 1987). Bartlett doubted whether any syllable is totally nonsensical, since even the sounds "Oh" or "Ah" can have associations for different individuals, and each association will affect the manner in which they are recalled.

He started his investigations by telling stories and by showing pictures and inkblots to a large number of subjects and later asking them to describe their memories of what they had heard or seen. It is interesting to find that his work, first published by Cambridge University Press in 1932, was reissued—unchanged by that press in 1995 apart from an introduction and a biographical sketch, because it was seen as having enormous contemporary importance.

Bartlett measured changes and distortions in memory over periods of time, from a few minutes to ten years, and found that there were major changes—omissions, additions, and distortions. Some of the distortion, it seemed, was caused by personal or world events at the time, as with the man who, during World War I, was shown a stylized picture of a pointing hand[1] at the bottom of a page and an aircraft in the sky at the top of the page—but who recalled the picture, many years later, not as a hand but as an antiaircraft gun aiming at the plane.

The study is also interesting in that Bartlett's work on the interpretation of pictures and inkblots long preceded that of Murray and Rorschach, and it has influenced modern thought on memory and perception far more than most of us realize! Mollon suggests that memory distortion, often called a Bartlett effect, may even influence our perception of past theories of psychotherapy, such as some of the theories of Sigmund Freud (P. Mollon, personal communication, 1999).

It sometimes seems that music helps enhance the accuracy of difficult memories. But this is an opinion based upon many observations rather than on hard-line research.

Emotional Trauma and Its Effects on Remembering

The memory problems we are considering here, however, are not those associated with brain damage but problems resulting from emotional and psychological trauma. We usually think of the memory as totally reliable, believing that if we are not afflicted by dementia or other brain damage

- we shall be able to retrieve important memories;
- if we remember something, it did really happen;
- memories of events will be recalled exactly as they happened;
- if someone tells us something, we shall retell it with complete accuracy;
- if something terrible and traumatic happens to us, we shall be able to describe it;
- eventually, painful memories cease to trouble us.

Bartlett's research (1932/1995) showed that our memories are influenced by our personal views of life and our perceptions of the event, and, depending on our perceptions, memories change over time. Later work on memory showed that

- apparent memories can be manufactured by a therapist's processes, with no intention of deceiving, although the process may be influenced by the therapist's private agenda (Mollon, 1998, pp. 7–8);
- memories of events can be suppressed and later recovered, and there are accounts in which corroborative evidence proved that these were true recovered memories (Mollon, 1998, pp. 37–39);
- memory suppression may be associated with dissociative disorder that occurs when the victim of abuse deals with it by separating that aspect from other aspects of the personality (Mollon, 1998, pp. 75–77).

Questions on Memory

Why Do People Repress Terrible Memories but Later Get Them Back?

It may be that childhood abuse is "forgotten" because of the child's need for material support, but that later in adult life it is safe to recall the unhappiness when an event triggers the memory. Music may provide that trigger. Recall is also observed to occur when, for example, a woman's life mirrors in some way the time from the past, as when a child reaches the age at which the mother was abused.

Most therapists recognize that memories presented to us as "fact" may be delusional or fantasy, such as Munchausen syndrome. Sometimes they are intended to impress, but sometimes they are a symptom of a desperate need for acceptance and attention, born of childhood neglect and rejection. Memories may be distorted because of a current crisis; they may be therapist-led—out of the sometimes unrecognized personal agenda of the therapist; they may be unduly influenced by experiences and environmental factors dating from the time the memory was laid down, and so on. But there may be external evidence that supports the veracity of memories, such as were described with "Susan" (Bright, 1999b), whose pseudohallucinations corresponded strikingly with those known to occur in adult survivors of childhood sexual abuse.

Why Do People Need to Describe False Memories? Is It Entirely the Responsibility of the Therapist Concerned?

I believe that insufficient time has been given to the needs of those who "recover" false memories. Perhaps there is a desperate need for attention or the false memories are a projective defense mechanism to deal with shameful wishes. False memories may be delusional beliefs arising from a psychiatric disorder. To place all the responsibility or "blame" on the therapist is to deflect attention from the desperate needs of those who "remembered."

Why Are Memories Suppressed, When People with Post-Traumatic Stress Disorder Cannot Stop Remembering Traumatic Events That Actually Happened?

Our brains sort out and store memories of recent events, and we store our memories in a form our minds can handle (van der Kolk & van der Hart, 1991). But when trauma is extreme, the hippocampus is impaired (Bremner et al., 1995), and because of chemical changes that follow, the normal sorting-out process cannot take place. The memories remain frozen in a different part of the brain from where storage normally occurs. The result is that we cannot remove the largely sensory memories from the conscious mind; they interrupt our lives and interfere with normal consciousness.

Brain research on post-traumatic stress disorder revealed that reliving the trauma has profound effects upon the cortex, one result being that the area of the brain concerned with expressive speech (Broca's area) shuts down when the trauma is reexperienced under laboratory conditions (van der Kolk, 1998, pp. 383–399). Possibly this is why music, coming mainly from the right hemisphere, may be useful: nonverbal communication through music therapy provides a means to therapy and, one hopes a way of facilitating resolution.

Various ways of dealing with traumatic, ever present memories have been used: imploding by repeated recollection, rapid eye movement desensitization, and so on. Their use has met with some success, but none of the methods works for everyone, and the imploding ("flooding") technique has been shown to be harmful for some people (Solomon, Gerrity, & Muff, 1992).

The Common Effects of Most Childhood Sexual Abuse: A Summary

Childhood sexual abuse brings many griefs and losses:

- Loss of childhood—innocence, fun, freedom from fear
- Enforced sexual experiences and inappropriate arousal
- Physical injury by intromission
- Loss of self-esteem
- Guilt (van der Kolk, 1997)
- Difficulties with anger and self-assertion
- Destruction of or hazards to future sexual happiness
- Fear of people
- General loss of trust
- Fear of intimacy of any kind
- For boys, the strong risk of themselves becoming abusers (Gabbard, 1994, p. 300)
- For girls, the equally strong risk that they will become attached to abusive men (Gabbard, 1994, p. 300)

Gabbard alerts us to possible emotional manipulation of therapists by pedophiles in order to gain acceptance of their behavior (Gabbard, 1994, pp. 344–346).

Practicalities in Work with Women Who Have Been Sexually Abused

Firsthand accounts of the responses of incestuously abused children have been published, and the books are useful for all grief therapists, giving greater depth to one's empathic understanding of the client's needs (Galey, 1988).

The extent to which insight-based music therapy, such as the interpretation of improvisation, is appropriate will depend on the client's own strengths. For some, all we can do is support and validate suppressed feelings of anger, betrayal, confusion, and fear. There are risks in psychotherapeutic interventions with those who have been sexually abused as children when the client feels uncertain as to what may and may not be spoken about. This uncertainty can undermine the client's desperate attempts to keep the mind under control (Mollon, 1998, p. 90).

As with bereavement by death, the therapist needs to start with an open mind, avoiding preliminary suppositions as to the client's feelings. For most women the sexual exploitation experienced in childhood was frightening, repulsive, and in some instances, painful. But this is not true for all. If someone is referred for therapy after incest or if this experience emerges unexpectedly during a session, to start by saying, "How terrifying for you!" makes it impossible for the woman to disclose secret feelings of ambivalence about her father's behavior.

When working with adults who were incestuously abused as children by their father (or by the mother's partner), anger appears to be directed as much at the mother who failed to protect or act upon the child's expressed fears, as at the abusive male. It is important therefore that we keep the door open for allowing anger to be described, avoiding the assumption that it is directed only toward the abuser. Open-ended statements are more effective than questions or instructions, as the following examples demonstrate.

- "Sometimes people feel very bewildered about what has happened to them, not sure why it happened or what they really felt about it."
- "I find that children who were sexually abused have sometimes been made to feel that it is their fault even though it was absolutely *not* their fault."
- "Many people say they cannot understand why their mother did not protect them from abuse and feel really angry about it."
- "I, myself, get really angry at what some children/adults had to endure, and I'm sad for them in their loneliness and fear because they couldn't tell anyone how they felt."
- "People who have been sexually abused are sometimes left quite numb, not sure what they ought to feel."

I have found it unnecessary and unhelpful to encourage detailed accounts of the abuse, that to deal with the overall effects rather than the minutiae helps to prevent the client becoming "stuck forever" in the memories and yet allows the feelings associated with the memories (anger, guilt, shame, fear) to emerge. I do not, however, have any research to support this view. It remains a clinical observation.

Not all sexual abuse occurs in childhood, adults too are traumatized by unwanted sexual intercourse. We know that sexual abuse, humiliation, and torture are tools for political repression, and women refugees have described sexual intercourse with cruelty in truly horrifying circumstances.

Improvising angry music can be helpful. This can be by a reflective method or later, when trust is established, as a shared experience—where the therapist can use the accompaniment to prevent the client from being overwhelmed, while still giving opportunity to acknowledge and express emotion.

Expressing It All in Music

Each therapist develops a style of interacting, and we make constant therapeutic decisions in the course of any interaction, whatever our field of expertise! The decision as to how to express the hidden emotions in music is made on the basis of observations of the client, changes in posture and other body language, what has been said or left unsaid, speech intonation, pitch, tension, and the age and musical preference of the client.

No guidance can be given here, but we need skills in improvisation and a wide repertoire. Nothing is more destructive to the alliance than for the therapist to spend minutes flipping through a songbook deciding what to play or sing while chances for intimacy evaporate!

Two Vignettes

- Helen, a resident in a rehabilitation unit for people with mild alcohol-related brain damage, had been admitted in her early forties and was referred to me for the management of her grief over a recent divorce. We started with music from her teenage years, when life had been fun, but one song brought back memories of an outing with a new boyfriend that ended in gang rape by him with a group of his friends. Helen cried and trembled while disclosing these events, with an aura of shame as she spoke of her fears. Later, after receptive improvisation had been played to symbolize sadness and loss, she disclosed that, after this rape experience, she had found herself repulsed by sexual intercourse. She had married because, "I thought that, with someone you loved, it would be different. But it wasn't." She then said it was only by becoming intoxicated that she could tolerate sexual relations with her husband. This eventually wrecked the marriage.

  Helen's grief was complex and her emotional response to the divorce was ambivalent because it brought feelings of relief at the end of sexual intercourse, but also of failure—"I should have been able to cope." We played music together, Helen playing bongo drums rather than the keyboard. The impairment of the cerebellum, that part of the brain concerned with coordination, which was damaged by her many years of hazardous use of alcohol, made coordination difficult so that drumming was the only possibility. The cerebellar damage also affected her so that she had "scanning speech," in which words and emphasis were not clearly delineated, and singing proved unsatisfactory, but her speech was intelligible. Although songwriting was not included in the six weeks of music therapy because of impaired competence and fears of failure, we improvised on thoughts that another person might have included in a song.

The outcome was good. Permission to express anger and other feelings through music therapy, together with counseling from members of the team and me, led to a positive relationship with a fellow resident. They both participated in AA groups within the hospital and community and set up a good relationship with a shared AA sponsor. Eventually they entered into marriage, in which sex was, for the first time, a happy experience for both.

- Margaret was admitted to the hospital in her mid-twenties with serious suicidal ideation and multiple attempts. She had been a sex worker since her early teens, had been involved in an abusive partnership with a man by whom she had a child (currently in foster care), and was a heroin user. The referral requested music therapy for grief resolution as a means of support as she tried to accept the need to change and to deal with her emotions about the way her life had been. The emotion that Margaret disclosed during music therapy sessions was primarily anger with her mother for not protecting her from incestuous sexual abuse in childhood. It seemed probable that her destructive lifestyle was, at least in part, the outcome of that abuse and sexual exploitation.

  Because of lethargy caused in part by her depression, most of our music therapy was receptive. Margaret's feelings were validated through both familiar and improvised music. As with many other clients, Margaret chose as her personal theme the music from the film *Chariots of Fire*, and we spoke of being willing to meet and accept challenges to change. We also talked of the need to tolerate confrontation, since this was a feature of some of our sessions. At times Margaret was inclined to adopt a "poor me" attitude to absolve her from making any efforts for herself.

  Over many weeks, Margaret achieved empathic understanding of her mother's fear of her de facto husband and thereby realized that her mother was too frightened to confront her partner with what was happening. Being herself a survivor of childhood abuse, Margaret's mother was unable to readily initiate actions that would have prevented the continuation of the abuse experienced by her little girl. The comment that revealed the extent of the young woman's change in attitude and the extent of her forgiveness was, "Poor old Mum, she was just scared shitless and didn't know what to do about it!" spoken in what seemed to be a tone of tender affection.

Our sessions also included practical discussion about parenting skills, which Margaret lacked, and included learning childhood songs that she hoped one day to sing to her child.

Margaret continued to have difficulties coping with her emotions, and there were many noisy and physically violent protests when her requests for medication to blot these out were refused, despite the staff giving explanations about the need to avoid simply blotting out the difficult feelings. Ultimately, however, she was able to accept the need of not resorting to chemically induced numbness.

These aggressive protests and eventual acceptance were symbolic of the young woman's struggle to move away from having her identity entirely invested in being a victim, and instead accept her identity as a young woman who was gradually coping with life despite having experienced difficulties. This was a vital step for her because there is a high risk of revictimization in those who have been abused. Gabbard (1994, p. 300) comments that there are gender differences in this matter. Women who have been abused tend to become attached to abusive men, whereas men and boys who were abused tend to identify with their abusers and themselves become abusers.

Any personal unresolved feelings about sexual relationships, victimization, gender, and power must not be allowed to get in the way of effective therapy. Gabbard described a therapist who became so committed to the stories of ritual satanic sexual abuse and childbirth told by his client, that he lost sight of reality-testing and denied evidence by a gynecologist that showed indisputably that neither childbirth nor sexual abuse of the nature described could possibly have taken place (Gabbard, 1994, pp. 307–308). This incident is a warning—to anyone who works in this field—of the risks of allowing a therapist's credulity and personal needs to take precedence over other considerations.

- Susan, the victim of particularly damaging sexual abuse, has already been described as someone for whom outcome was good despite having had only two face-to-face music therapy sessions. In those sessions and the work she later completed, it was clear that she had moved on from being a victim to being someone with real future potential (Bright, 1999b). An important feature that demonstrated the changes in her life was the composition (after discharge) of the words to a song symbolizing the changes she achieved in music therapy. This song was then set to music in the style we had previously discussed.

Summary

The practicalities of working in music therapy for resolution of grief and trauma following sexual abuse can be summarized thus:

- Know yourself. Understand your own attitudes toward sex and gender to avoid following your own private agenda while apparently helping clients with theirs.
- Do your homework on memory and its different manifestations.
- Do your homework on sexual abuse and its aftereffects.
- Recognize the overwhelming fears and anxieties that clients may be hiding, no matter how long ago the abuse occurred.
- Be sure that clients feel that the session is under control, that feelings will not be allowed to overwhelm them.
- Avoid setting the emotional climate before you know what the client's feelings really are.
- Choose the style of music intervention to be used according to the personality and the needs of the client: familiar music to evoke past memories, although this may cause further harm, since for some people reliving trauma is damaging (Solomon, et al., 1992), or improvised music to validate blocked emotions.
- Have the empathy and skill to know whether and when catharsis of blocked emotions should occur and to what extent, whether through words, music, or both.

The interventions that arise from our attitudes, knowledge, and competency will include some of the following:

- Life history
- Validation of the feelings resulting from the abuse. This is best achieved through verbal intervention, sketches, a life road map, and receptive and shared improvised music.
- Further interaction to look at the client's self-perception
- Steps to move away from victimization and into a series of new self-perceptions as a recovering victim, a recovered victim, and then to a normal person who can recall abuse but for whom this is no longer *the* life agenda.

The steps may include improvisation in music, songwriting, movement with music, formal or informal graphic art, keeping a journal, and any other appropriate means of achieving change.

Knowing Ourselves

Although we need to understand ourselves in all work in music therapy, it is of particular importance in working with those who have been sexually abused. Music therapists who work with those who have reportedly suffered from CSA can themselves experience internal sadness, anger, conflict, bewilderment, and many other emotions as they try to sort out what really happened or did not happen.

Before accepting a referral for such work, when sexual abuse has already been disclosed or is suspected by the referring professional, we need to understand ourselves and our attitudes on matters relating to sex, gender preference, relationships, power and powerlessness, and so on. It is essential that we do not find ourselves at the mercy of an unrecognized private agenda on any of the matters listed above.

We must also establish boundaries for our work in this area:

- Avoid questions that probe so deeply into details of abuse that they may lead the client to become so disturbed by memories that it becomes impossible to move into a more normal way of living.
- Avoid evoking false memories.
- Avoid acting in such a way that the client becomes set in the lifelong role of "victim."

Establishing a strong therapeutic alliance seems to help maintain these boundaries because it has the ethos of "we are in this together."

Mollon's book, cited in several places in this chapter, is a helpful publication. It is based on sound professional knowledge and an objective, scientific attitude, and presents a balanced view based upon these rather than on emotionalism. It also provides therapists with information and ideas on how to equip themselves to work in the troubled area of sexual abuse (1998, pp. 7–11, also chapter 10 on guidelines).

Ongoing professional supervision with someone who is familiar with the type of work is also necessary. Someone from another discipline with expert knowledge will generally be more helpful than a music therapist who knows little about the challenges of working in therapy with those who have been sexually abused.

Chapter 8

The Griefs of Disability and Long-Term Losses at All Ages

Aims and learning objectives of this chapter:

- *Become familiar with the effects of physical functioning, emotional and social health, and happiness that are experienced through health problems present at birth or arising later in life*
- *Become familiar with the griefs and losses that affect people's lives at all stages, personally in bereavement and social isolation, and environmentally in ageism, discrimination, and powerlessness*
- *Achieve an appropriate known repertoire of songs and other musical items from each decade period of the 1900s and up to the present day to meet the needs of the population*
- *Develop appropriate skills in songwriting and improvisation, adapting to each person's needs*
- *Continue to increase skills in observation of behavior, in empathic counseling and all psychotherapeutic approaches appropriate for the people with whom one works*
- *Continue to develop personal skills in building and maintaining a therapeutic alliance*
- *Build interdisciplinary relationships in order to educate self and others, and maximize the benefits of music therapy to our clients*
- *Contradictory though this may seem in the context of grief therapy, allow oneself and the client the opportunity for fun!*

What Needs Do We Meet, and How Do We Meet Them?

There is much in common between the needs of persons with disability and their families, no matter what their ages. We see sadness and disappointment at unfulfilled hopes. We notice guilty feelings, often complicated by religious beliefs, about the circumstances or illness that led to the disability or about the birth of an impaired child. Hearing of the grief still unresolved in later life also tells us of the lifelong harm that was done to some people in blocking their expression of emotion. We observe anger. These emotions are common to all ages, with variants arising from ethnic origin, spiritual attitudes, age, education, and upbringing.

On a few occasions we may be surprised by expressions of relief, as with the young man who said that his quadriplegia—the outcome of a delusional belief that he could fly out of an upper window—had given him greater stability and peace than he had previously experienced, "No more decisions to be made—ever!" This may or may not have proven to be true, but it was certainly how he saw it. Relief was felt by the parents of a difficult young man, also quadriplegic, who felt that he had returned to being their little boy once more when an accident had made him totally dependent on them. Their worries over his care were as nothing compared with the worries they had previously experienced over his behavior.

Relief may also be expressed by the family of someone, who after many failed attempts has finally completed suicide, or when death has ended the life of someone whose behavior has been so destructive that the family has lost hope or realistic expectation that change will occur. Can we avoid being shocked by this sense of relief, and instead empathize with the past tragic experiences, the grief over lost hope, and the present sad realization that death has brought relief rather than sorrow?

When a disability has severely limited the participation of a family member or the spouse in active life and relationships, we frequently see bewilderment and fear, sometimes anger, about the role changes that follow the disability. Can we allow people to be angry? We may find this difficult, especially when there is anger with health professionals for not having prevented the problems.

The young wife of a man with serious brain trauma, whose injuries have caused major changes in personality and behavior, needs enormous support coping with the changes that must take place in her life and the lives of any of her children. Depending on the severity of the situation, she may need help—usually given by social workers, with support from other professionals as well—in bringing the marriage to an end. Can we support such a decision or does it conflict with our views on marriage?

A young man's father and mother, on the other hand, may be able to revert to the parental role of early childhood and accept responsibility for support and care. Sadly, the young man himself is frequently prevented by the brain impairment from understanding why life should be different in the future, and this loss of insight is yet another source of grief. The song "Yesterday" was requested by a man whose wife had left him because his new violence following a head injury made continued marriage impossible. He had no insight into this and found that the song expressed for him his bewilderment and confusion.

The male partner of a woman so severely disabled by an illness or an accident that there is little prospect of improvement and institutional life is required, has multifaceted grief at the loss of companionship and their normal sexual, loving relationship. He may also be anxious about the tasks of learning to live alone, with all that this implies, practically and emotionally. All these may be worsened by anxieties over finances. On top of all these, he has the beginnings of doubt as to how long she will live, and how long he wants her to live. Do such feelings frighten us as we look into the future? Can we cope with the emotions we see in clients and families? We may need to rethink our own current attitudes.

The age of the affected individual can make a difference. There may be differences in responses to an older person who has developed a degenerative condition such as Alzheimer's disease compared with feelings about a young person who has had an accident or an illness in which improvement may be expected. We tend to feel differently about a major disability or illness that is seen as untimely, as when a young person has a chronic disease such as cystic fibrosis, compared with responses to an older person dying as the result of Parkinson's disease, who is seen as having lived a good, long life.

If someone has suffered an injury or developed an illness that may *appear* to be self-imposed—a car accident from drunken driving, an overdose of an illicit "recreational" drug, HIV-AIDS acquired, not through a faulty blood transfusion but through unsafe sexual practices or needle sharing—can we relate warmly to the individual? Can we take a step back from our own ethical or moral position in order to relate empathically to that person?

A patient came into my music room one day saying truculently, "I hope you're not a Christian." My reply was to say gently, "Tell me why that is important for you?" He answered, "If you *are* a Christian, you'll disapprove of me because I've got AIDS." My answer was, "Well, I *am* a Christian, but that doesn't mean I disapprove of you. All kinds of things can lead to someone having AIDS. And anyway Jesus was always trying to help those whose lives had got in a muddle for some reason, so let's just see if we can work comfortably together!" We did that, with a very satisfactory outcome in his feelings about himself, even though his illness was not responding well to treatment.

Our understanding of what life is like for people of any age who have been adversely affected by illness, change, and loss is necessarily secondhand. We can never say with any justification, "I know how you feel," because we don't. (I clearly recall being concussed at age 8, after a fall from a pony, and remember my fear and bewilderment when people in the hospital could not understand what I was saying, even though I thought I was talking sense. This memory is still so vivid it gives me some insight into what it may be like to have jargon aphasia, in which a stroke causes someone to use inappropriate words or neologisms, but also prevents the person from knowing that the words are meaningless (Bright, 1996, p. 49).

Meeting musical needs also requires knowledge and skills, and we may need to make more use of precomposed and less of improvised music. If we work with people who are confused mentally because of dementia or trauma, it is important to reach them initially through music that they already know. But for people whose abstract thinking is intact (such as those with spinal injuries), improvised music helps to express the inexpressible for them.

If we are observant and empathic, if we extend our technical expertise by appropriate reading (including non-music therapy publications), we become more skilled and more understanding with the passage of time, developing our understanding of the physical, social, and emotional hazards that can mar later life. Understanding the background of the person's life will help us deal with the disorder, no matter what its nature. Our knowledge of responses to grief and our gift of empathy will support us in our efforts to help.

What Equipment Do We Need?

The chapter is written with the expectation that the music therapist will not depend upon recorded music but will play a portable musical instrument that can be taken to the bedside or chair side. An electric keyboard with its range of tones, the piano accordion with its capability of playing a clear melody line, or, for those who have strong singing voices with a wide tonal range, the Autoharp or guitar are all very suitable. There are music therapists who play single-line orchestral instruments, but a chordal instrument has some advantages, in giving a harmonic support to the voice.

For younger people we also need a good quality cassette player that will accept CDs as well as the ordinary tape cassettes, because modern pop music is generally performed by a large group of instruments with effects we cannot produce at the bedside or chair side. Guitarists are at an advantage, but they too may occasionally feel inadequate when unfamiliar items are requested!

We need a known repertoire of music for a better chance of being able to respond to particular requests. Requests will be modified by nationality, ethnicity, social, spiritual, and educational experience as well as by age. Gathering our repertoire together is helped by the ability to play by ear, so that we can reproduce songs we hear only a few times. The one disadvantage of learning songs from a client is if that client sings it with an error, we shall reproduce that error whenever we perform it. It is extremely hard to correct the rendition if one has played something for several years before discovering a wrong note has been played all that time. But this disadvantage is outweighed by the benefit to the client of the role reversal—the unusual experience of teaching the therapist!

Various books are available from which we can learn items by heart or use as resources at the bedside to offer someone a choice if they cannot suggest a title. These are listed and annotated in the bibliography.

In work for older people, there is a tendency to group them all together, forgetting that in any facility there may be a generation's difference in ages, from the young-old in their late sixties to the very old who may have lived for nearly one hundred years. Their recollections of music—the songs they sang, the musical shows they saw, the performers they remember, the film music they recall—will be as different from each other as are those of the so-called baby boomers from those of the heavy-metal devotees!

For younger people, too, there are fashions and trends. Familiarity with music is often determined by age, although there are some songs that are quasi-classics, known by people across several generations.

Ethnicity, even in long-established migrants, affects preference for music. Those who are long-term residents may yet yearn for music from the original homeland at times of crisis, mourning, anxiety, or other difficulty.

It is also useful to have resource books available when working with older people, preferably in large print, because the therapist's "What song would you like me to play for you?" may be met by a total blank because of memory loss, or its polite substitute, "I'll leave that to you, dear. You know better than I do!" To have a songbook ready with an easily read index can be useful in jogging the memory and starting the process of reminiscence, "Oh yes, *that* one; I remember my mother singing that!" The Ulverscroft Large Print Songbooks are useful for this method of giving choice.

These songbooks and our other resources are not, of course, a means in themselves but the means to an end—that end being to create an atmosphere in which matters can be safely recalled, disclosed, and discussed. The pain and complexity of these may lie in past losses—in the contrast between past happiness and present sadness, in fears for the future, and in the difficulties of adaptation to change and loss. Sometimes I am asked, "When will I get back to normal?" and the answer is often, "I am not sure how long it will take, but I do know that it will be a *different* normal."

What Personal Skills and Approaches Are Needed to Create an Atmosphere for Disclosure and Conversation?

Sometime in the 1980s, I conducted a group session in a psychogeriatric ward where nursing staff tended to change so often patients were often addressed as "dear" because the nurses did not know their names. Because of my concern about this, while yet empathizing with nurses whose rosters changed so frequently that learning names was indeed difficult, I planned a forty-minute session focused on individual identity and songs that included individual names, to facilitate the use of the names of those present.

I had started the program by singing a welcoming song to each person by name, going around the circle, touching each person's hand and singing, "Good morning, Mrs. ______, it's nice to see you here. Good morning, good morning to you."[1] I ended the session in much the same way except that the music I played while walking around the circle was a farewell song sung to each person individually. As I finished the session, I heard (in a penetrating whisper) "Wasn't that lovely, she used my name!"

Whether we use first names or a formal approach will depend on the ethos of the time, the philosophy of the unit, and the age and attitude of each person. Clearly the "dear" approach is inadequate, and formality suggests personal dignity, but the dementing person may have forgotten that she is Mrs. ______ and, if she is able to think in terms of names and identity, may have returned to thinking of herself by her unmarried name, as Miss (Maiden-name) and the married title may be confusing. For such people the first name may in fact be the most helpful.

The music we have to offer, the way we introduce the idea of songwriting as a means to personal expression, the instruments we offer or have available, and even our style of dress, all combine to evoke a casual, friendly atmosphere in which thoughts and feelings can easily be shared.

In a traumatic brain injury unit, with people from ages sixteen to about forty-five, we had a wonderful afternoon filling drink bottles with water to different levels so that each one produced a note of a different pitch when struck with a drumstick. We then made up tunes to be played on these and finally made up some words for a simple song contrasting things that were good with things that were bad, each of us taking turns to suggest new lines for the song. The activity was presented in such a way that it was acceptable to all the patients, no matter what their ages. Not every group would enjoy this, but some other groups may find it has possibilities for being both funny and expressive of quite deep feelings.

When Might Individual Work Result from Group Work?

In this chapter particularly, it is assumed that the music therapist is working not as a recreation director but as a therapist who accepts referrals for individual work at a deeply personal level.

Group work in music therapy may, however, appear recreational despite having a foundation of therapeutic intent. The aims may be to promote tolerance for the differing views of others, willingness to take turns with preferred instruments, support for the withdrawn, and recognition of the achievements of another, as well as to observe a need for individual work.

One recognizes the need for one-to-one work when one sees a paradoxical response: a particular item of "happy" music leads to one person crying openly or trying to hide tears, while others are smiling, laughing, and talking cheerfully about the memories evoked by the music. Or one person leaves the room, or asks to be taken out, showing signs of anger or distress as a piece is played or sung.

The empathic music therapist sees the behavior and responds appropriately. When we talk after the group is over, we need enough time and enough privacy for extended confidential conversation and probably additional music (whether familiar or improvised)—not simply the odd minute or two of bland reassurance in the passageway as others walk past.

A useful comment to open the discussion is "I couldn't help seeing that (name of song) upset you. I wondered whether you'd find it useful to talk about it for a few minutes?"[2] The reply may be "I don't want to talk about it," usually accompanied by loss of eye contact. Although we may feel that the problem thus remains an unexploded time bomb waiting to detonate and that avoidant behavior has its own risks, we cannot force confidences. So our answer is probably one of acceptance, and we remind the person of our availability.

Vignette

Such was the case for an elderly woman, recently widowed and hospitalized for some time, who looked back in grief at the birth of her son (seriously impaired in body and mind), whom she and her husband had cared for at home for fifty years. Now, however, her ill-health had made this impossible, and she grieved for this and also for past unhappiness when little support was available for parents of handicapped children except encouragement to "get rid of him" as she put it.[3] She also felt she had failed by becoming too frail to care for him.

It would have been easy to adopt the attitude of "Don't be silly. Of course you haven't failed. Your son will be okay in the group home he's gone to. Don't worry so much; just concentrate on your own health!" But this was not what she needed. She needed permission to be sad, to talk of her son, to express anger at past attitudes of rejection of people with handicaps, to voice anxiety about his future care, and to feel that her own loving care for him at home had been worthwhile. Only then could she focus upon her own current needs.

This change was achieved through singing together the songs she had sung to her son at different stages of his life, smiling together over some of the mistakes he made with the words; these were mistakes from childhood misinterpretation, not a consequence of his disability, so it was okay to smile about them. Gradually she was reassured about the group home, that her son would have individual care and be helped to cope with life without her. The fact that I was involved with providing music therapy in one such group home probably helped!

Griefs

Griefs from the past may include many different events and losses:

- The wayward son or daughter who died from a car accident because he or she was drunk at the time, and the nearness of one's own death renews that grief as one realizes the family is now diminished or will die out

- The husband who came back from the Vietnam War so changed that marriage became impossible, and music elicits memories of hopes that were unfulfilled
- The adult child whose marriage failed and now the grandparents no longer see their grandchildren; they recall their earlier hopes for ongoing family relationships
- The dementing illness that deprived the spouse of the partner's company and constant affection, so that the survivor sadly looks back on the happier past and grieves over the newer realization that hopes for retirement and old age will not be met
- The death of the grandchild from childhood cancer; past hopes are recalled with grief, and the need to change the will, the testamentary dispositions, is thus a tragic necessity

Griefs of the present are also varied:

- The young parents whose child is born with a major impairment such as will lead to expensive medical treatment in early childhood, if the child survives, followed by a need for constant care at home or life in an institution, with serious disability and handicap
- A newly acquired disability in a young adult, from illness or accidental injury, that reduces hopes for continued independence and causes social isolation, reducing the chance of normal adult life, marriage, and parenthood
- A major disability later in life that mars happiness at home or makes it necessary that one partner leaves the marital home to live in a nursing home, with sadness, loneliness, and all the other emotions found in either situation
- Bereavement
- Fears about terminal or chronic illness, of oneself or another
- Dementia of spouse or another; the impact of this can affect people in one, two, or even three generations
- The grief that follows confirmation of the fear that oneself is developing dementia
- Financial anxiety, which may or may not be reality-based
- Sensory deficits such as loss of hearing or sight, which cause loss of independence and social isolation
- An accident to a child or the birth of a grandchild with an impairment that will lead to disability and handicap
- The death or serious illness of an adult child or grandchild
- The loss, through relocation, of an adult child

- The loss of an attribute or a skill that does not threaten independence but causes sadness and disappointment

Vignettes

The following vignettes demonstrate how music, empathic counseling based upon professional knowledge, human understanding, interdisciplinary teamwork, and practical interventions are used to help people of all ages with disabilities.

- The older woman in the surgical ward, after requesting a song from her courtship, cried and then went on to say abruptly, "Of course I have to wear a bag now." She had used this song request to lead into open discussion of her private needs because she needed to talk about her recent colostomy and her fears that her husband would find her physically repulsive so that sex would no longer be enjoyable. This may have been in part a projection of her feelings of revulsion about her body image.

  We spoke about this at length and with her approval and after discussion with the nursing unit manager, arrangements were made for the colostomy nurse-specialist to visit her while still hospitalized, and in home visits after discharge. This is usually standard procedure but had somehow not been arranged.

- Another woman, noted for ringing her bedside bell at frequent intervals without any obvious need to do so, and for her impatience when the bell was not answered immediately, listened to some music from her earlier life. She then described how happy she had been in her nursing home, how she had been hospitalized for a hip replacement, which had become infected and so was removed, and how disappointing this was.

  She also expressed anger because due to her prolonged absence she had lost her bed in the nursing home, and she had very real and justified fears for the future. She needed to be allowed to talk about these at length, and the music therapist had more time to spare than the nurses.

  Talking them through did solve the problems to some extent, as did singing together the requests she made for music from her more active past, which gave permission for sadness to be ventilated. A further intervention was to arrange for one of the young nurses to come each hour on the hour, whether or not the patient rang her bell, and make her laugh!

  The stimulus to laughter included dancing a Highland Fling, singing a humorous song, telling a joke, and so on. But most significant of all in diminishing the bell-ringing behavior was the knowledge that she would be visited every hour for about two or three minutes, whether or not she rang her bell. The result was that nursing staff found the patient less tiresome to deal with. Her social worker also found her easier to cope with, as efforts were made to find her a bed in a nursing home that would measure up to the alleged perfection of the previous establishment.

The Individual as Part of a Social Group

One elderly man was so angry about his lack of visitors that I was asked to see him about it because nursing staff saw this as an expression of grief and not simply difficult behavior. I found that his roommate in their shared accommodation was often visited by many adult children and even more numerous grandchildren, and this heightened his own disappointment that his wife had not been able to bear children so he could never have grandchildren visit him. This was actually more a source of distress to him than his own impending death from cancer, and he revealed that the family dying out was an enormous grief to him because of his Jewish background and traditions and because of his memories of time in a concentration camp when the thought of family survival was a source of hope.

But many people do have family members who are able to visit, and it can be helpful to work jointly in music therapy with client and family. This is important because an acquired disability alters family—and particularly marital—relationships.

- After a man suffered a major impairment from stroke, his wife, who had previously been happily dependent on her husband for financial management, driving, care, and general decision making, found the change of role from dependency to management difficult to accept. She antagonized some staff by demanding that the time of rehabilitation be extended beyond what was reasonable. It seemed that it was easier to cope when her husband was clearly defined as a patient and she saw herself as providing support on a temporary basis only, and she also had unrealistic hopes that continued rehabilitation would restore him to previous levels of functioning. She was invited to join the music therapy group so she could work cooperatively with him in various ways, listen together to their old favorite and significant music, and have the opportunity to share in discussion with other couples who were in the process of adapting to changed circumstances.
- A man in his forties spent every afternoon with his little daughter in a traumatic brain injury unit. When mowing the lawn, a stone had flown up and penetrated the child's brain, leading to extraordinarily severe and extensive damage. His constant visiting seemed to be a way of coping with

guilt, and he needed to share in singing childhood songs with his daughter, one of the few times her behavior was peaceful. It was difficult for him to speak of his own emotions and because he was being seen by the chaplain as well as the doctor and the social worker, I focused on creating happy memories for him of their shared pleasure, to fortify him in the future. He said that he planned to leave his wife and devote his life to caring for the child, but a massive and irremediable brain infection supervened and the little girl died. Staff feelings were mixed between relief that an impossible situation was finished and grief at the father's continuing grief, guilt, and loss.

- As a consequence of a stroke, a man suffered from jargon aphasia, in which the speech has normal intonation and emphasis but the words are meaningless; he was unable to monitor his own speech, being unable to recognize that he was using nonsense words but thought he was talking complete sense. On many occasions he hit his wife with his fists for (as he thought) ignoring his comments and requests. Although intellectually she could accept the basis for his changed behavior, her distress was nevertheless intense and she required comfort and support as well as explanations from the speech pathologist and me. Joining in a small aphasia group and singing together was also helpful because it renewed her emotional links to her now difficult spouse.
- Early-onset Alzheimer's disease brings extra problems for many people: The husband of a woman who became demented in her mid-forties needed to disclose his guilt. Not realizing she was ill, he had been angry with her for washing underwear in the toilet instead of in the washbasin. His grief was greatly helped by personal music therapy and counseling.
- A younger man from central Europe, who had an above-knee amputation following an accident, disclosed in an individual music therapy session the difficulties he anticipated in sexual intercourse because of the loss of his leg, since he and his wife had only had sex in the "conventional" position and he doubted her willingness (and perhaps his own) to change. Practical aspects of this required exquisitely sensitive management. Although the matter was disclosed to me, I asked his (male) physician to bring the matter up "spontaneously" in discussion, especially because of ethnic and cultural issues, and the wife needed to be invited to joint counseling.
- The wife of a man with rapidly advancing dementia was noted by nursing staff as visiting too often. They believed that her daily prolonged visits arose from some element of guilt and asked me to see whether I could help her in this. I invited her to join with her husband in private music therapy sessions. During these sessions, they sang together their songs of courtship and reminisced about their life; the wife spoke of her painful back as being the

reason she could not care for her husband at home and said that it also made travel by public transport difficult, but that she "had to" come every day.

Empathic counseling after the session helped her to reveal that

- she had found her husband's increasingly demented behavior difficult to deal with at an emotional and practical level;
- he had developed hypersexuality that she had found distasteful;
- she had long wanted his admission to a long-term unit but felt guilty about this;
- his admission brought enormous relief, but her guilt about this led to constant visits, with fatigue and increasing back pain.

I reassured her that she was being quite normal and (after discussion with staff) said that it was okay to come on alternate days or just twice a week. This she accepted because she saw it as an official "instruction." I also suggested she join an Alzheimer support group where the topic of changed sexual behavior is a normal part of discussion and counseling.

Interestingly, the more relaxed attitude toward visiting improved interactions in the music therapy sessions, her husband's singing and conversation, and he agreed to record some comments about Air Force life and the song "Coming In on a Wing and a Prayer" for a radio broadcast on music therapy for reminiscence. This achievement also contributed to improved relationships between the couple.

We also see multiple disorders when there is, for example, both depression and dementia, and Barbara Beats wrote helpfully on the continuum of depression and dementia (1996). The occurrence of hallucinations is well documented in DLB, dementia with Lewy bodies (Gomez-Tortosa et al., 1998), but is not well known, and this form of dementia is sometimes mistaken for psychotic illness. Interestingly, a report describes brain changes in the visual cortex of a man with Lewy body dementia that were demonstrated by magnetic resonance imaging while he was experiencing visual hallucinations (Howard & David, 1997).

The spiritual needs of people with dementia and of their caregivers are too often neglected. Research has demonstrated the value that family caregivers place upon prayer as they cope with their complex and draining role (Stolley, Buckwalter, & Koenig, 1999). A Canadian music therapist has written most helpfully of ways in which the spiritual needs of people with dementia can be met through music-based work (Kirkland & McIlveen, 1999).

Relatives who share in music with a dementing relative and who see what appear to be miraculous responses need explanations that we have not cured the disease—all we have done is use music to open a temporary window into the person as he or she once was. And, sadly, the window must be reopened each time we meet.

There are reports of increased visual artistic skills and of musical skills in frontotemporal dementia (Miller, Cummings, Prince, Ponton, & Cotman, 1998; Miller, Boone, Cummings, Read, & Mishkin, 2000). Disappointingly, no description is given of the stage of dementia of the subjects, what is meant by musical skills, or how these were assessed. For this reason it is difficult to evaluate the significance of the reports to work in music therapy. Nevertheless, Miller's writings remind us of the possibility that changes in dementia (such as loss of previous inhibitions about musical performance) may enhance participation in music and enrich the life quality of persons with a dementing condition, especially in those whose nondominant hemisphere is largely intact.

The creation of poetry at the University of Stirling's (Scotland) Dementia Services similarly encourages us to be aware of artistic creativity in dementia, which may provide emotional release as people cope with their condition (Killick, 1997). One of these poems, "Grieving," tells us of the need to deal with long-ago grief, showing by its poignancy that dementia does not blot out painful memories of past tragedy. Through empathic music therapy we may be able to help resolve some of the emotional burden of remembered grief.

Amusia and Dysmusia

The following case history is given in detail, first because amusia and dysmusia are so closely linked with our own interests, and second because it demonstrates ideas that music therapists can put into effect in dysmusia, a condition that is rarely diagnosed but is probably not as rare as one might think (Bright, 1975).

Dorothy, a creative professional painter in an abstract, semi-impressionist style, an amateur pianist, and a composer, had a stroke at age 74, affecting the right (nondominant) hemisphere. She was found to have a left-sided hemiplegia, with increased muscular tone in the left arm and a claw deformity of the affected hand, so playing the piano was limited to her right hand. Initially she lost some vision due to loss of conjoint movement of the two eyes, but this improved later so reading music became easier. Her speech was dysarthric (slurring and weak). She was free of dysphasia (difficulty with use of verbal language) but had some dysphagia (difficulty in swallowing). Her poor hip-knee coordination, which made a four-pronged cane necessary for walking, added to her anger about dependency.

Music therapy assessment:

- Dorothy suffered from partial amusia, in that music had a reduced "meaning" for her, something that was hard for her to describe, but in subsequent sessions, the effects on her playing and composition were obvious.
- There was a change in her style of painting, observable but also disclosed by Dorothy herself during a subsequent music therapy session. She said

that her style of painting had changed from abstract to simplistic representation. She herself saw this as an improvement, as "communicating more directly with people," but most observers saw it as childish (as distinct from *childlike*, the former being usually a pejorative term denoting immaturity whereas the latter has connotations of innocence and joy).

The Grief of Amusia

Because the stroke affected the nondominant hemisphere, music therapy assessment included investigation of function as well as preference. At this initial assessment, the amusia was not obvious because Dorothy could read the notes of music, reproduce simple rhythmic patterns that were played for her, recognize and name intervals, and recognize and name previously known melodies. Subsequent work, however, revealed what she meant by lost "meaning" of music. She had, it seemed, lost musical creativity, so that her playing was limited to fair reproduction of what she heard, the quality depending upon the complexity of the items heard.

(An adult patient elsewhere who had undergone a [nondominant] hemispherectomy for intractable epilepsy also described her grief over the meaninglessness of music following surgery. She later hanged herself. Although she left no explanatory note, it was generally believed that the loss of music "feeling" had been significant in her decision to die. Dorothy, however, appeared not to be suicidal.)

An electric keyboard, bought for Dorothy by her family, was brought to sessions in the Rehabilitation Day Hospital. By placing our keyboards back-to-back, we played facing one another, not formally composed duets, but pieces already familiar to Dorothy. She played the melody while I accompanied this. She brought some songs from home that she had composed in the past, explaining that she had written the words and the melodies for these very musical and singable creations, but a professional arranger had completed the piano accompaniments, so it was clear her skills were chiefly lyrical.

Because Dorothy had her own keyboard, I suggested that she could enjoy doing some work at home. She composed some songs for our sessions, in vocal line only, but sadly, these lacked all the lyrical quality of her earlier works. The tunes consisted only of grammatically correct arpeggios. Although lacking variety, this method suited some themes, such as brisk martial or folk-dance type music, but it was emotionally irrelevant for thoughtful or contemplative ideas. These melodies were composed entirely visually and by rote—she analyzed the notes of the arpeggios alphabetically because she was unable to hear any tune in her head while doing the work. Although Dorothy was unable to analyze or describe what was wrong with her songs, she knew they lacked the earlier musicality and was bewildered and grief-stricken by the loss.

Because of the areas of brain that had been damaged, impairing her general capacity for abstraction, it was difficult to help Dorothy deal with her grief. She could not put her finger on what was wrong, and yet she knew that something was not right and was both angry and distressed. I had to work this through for myself, and empathy is especially complicated in the presence of brain damage because one has no idea what life feels like for the person concerned.

We persevered together, however, and our sessions extended from mid-January to mid-November, with a 2-month break in the middle. The high point for Dorothy was her composition of a song that was to be sung by staff members at the annual Christmas party. This was a jig, for which her quasi-military precision of rhythm and style worked well—the tune (as always) based on arpeggio structures. It was brisk and cheerful, and the staff group enjoyed rehearsing it, as she enjoyed being present at these practices. Her self-esteem benefited immeasurably from this, so that her grief was significantly lessened.

Unhappily, Dorothy suffered another stroke and died shortly before Christmas. The song was sung at the party, with mixed feelings of sadness and rejoicing—sadness that she did not attend the performance, but rejoicing that she had made sufficient recovery before her death to do the composition and that she herself rejoiced to know that it was to be performed.

Comments on the Case History

Amusia and Dysmusia: Causes and Effect

Although I referred to Dorothy's condition as "amusia" in my clinical notes at the time, it should have been described as "dysmusia" (analogous with aphasia and dysphasia, amenorrhea and dysmenorrhea) since there was a partial and not a complete loss of function. (The term *dysmusia* does not appear in any medical dictionary, but it should!)

Dorothy's rhythm and her ability to play notes correctly were intact; it was her lyricism and sense of wholeness that was lost. This was in contrast to what may appear a more disabling musical loss, that of rhythm. How much of this impairment was due to nondominant hemisphere musical impairment and how much to a parietal lesion cannot be determined. People who suffer from parietal damage commonly lose a sense of relationships and wholeness, in both spatial and abstract concepts (Critchley, 1953, chapters 8 and 9), and it may be that construction of melodies, making a lyrical "wholeness," depends upon intact competence in the parietal lobe of the brain. Some people appear to have a dysmusia when they have apraxia, that is, they no longer know how to perform planned movements, and this gives the impression of loss of music skills. But apraxia actually encompasses any *planned movement.*

The Grief of Dysmusia and Amusia

When music listening or performance or composition has been personally significant, the loss of function in amusia or dysmusia is particularly poignant. This was so for Dorothy.

Such a loss can impair relationships in which music has been important. The wife of one man with amusia described how their relationship had been altered by her husband's disorder. Earlier in their long married life, they shared interests in music; they attended operas, ballets, symphony concerts, and recitals, and in the evenings listened to favorite recordings. Now, however, music was a meaningless and unidentifiable jangle of sound and his grief over this was so intense that he could not tolerate any music in the home. They grieved about losing musical companionship. (Amusia and dysmusia may be especially difficult for a music therapist to deal with; perhaps it is too close to home?)

Skills Required and Tools Available

In working with grief resolution with people of any age who have a disability, we require a variety of skills: in music, in understanding the nature of the disabilities or disorders that we meet in our work, in personal relationships and counseling skills so that a therapeutic alliance is established, and in humor—we also need a sense of fun! Even in grief work, there are times of shared amusement and enjoyment.

In geriatrics, we must beware of stereotypes about aging. Not all people are impaired of memory; independence can be lost through physical handicap alone, leaving the mind alert and sharp. Multiple disorders require particular knowledge and skills. Even dementia is not a single condition. Behavior and cognitive function can vary enormously with the hundred and more different disorders that cause dementia. For example, paranoid behavior may occur, and relatives and staff may be accused of theft or other wrongdoing (Adams & Victor, 1993, p. 961). The European study on depression (EURODEP) revealed marked differences in criteria between *DSM-IV* and the tools used locally. This has led to the setting up of standardized criteria in order to overcome the confusion (Copeland et al., 1999).

There are various established rating scales for work with older people, which assist in our planning. The Cornell scale, described by Alexopoulos (Alexopoulos, Abrams, Young, & Shamoian, 1988) for measuring depression in the presence of dementia, is one such tool. This scale could be used to provide an indication as to whether depression in dementing persons had diminished over time as the consequence of music therapy. It is not unknown for depression to cause such severe cognitive impairment that it is perceived as dementia, but management of the depression reverses this (Rabins, Merchant, & Nestadt, 1984). Music therapy is seen to have such effects for some individuals.

Other scales assess the presence of agitation, and there are several that could be used in assessing the extent to which music therapy has brought changes in behavior. A measurement tool recently published usefully separates agitation from aggression on the grounds that aggression is not necessarily linked with agitation, but may arise from other causes (Kopecky & Yudofsky, 1999).

A Brief Look at Other Griefs and Challenges

In **Parkinson's disease** the challenges include

- difficulty walking because of dyskinesia;
- rigidity, whether of the cogwheel type, which inhibits movements, or what is called lead-pipe rigidity, with stiff movements;
- the tremor;
- the expressionless face and monotonous voice that belie the emotional life within;
- the dementia that develops in some people;
- the drug reactions that can occur.

Cerebrovascular accidents, whether a full-blown stroke or strokes-in-miniature, **Transient Ischemic Attacks** (TIAs), cause changes differing widely in severity and type:

- People with some damage to the dominant hemisphere may lose speech but understand what is said to them.
- Some, with more extensive damage, have global aphasia in which both expressive and receptive speech is lost.
- Most have some degree of motor function loss in the right side of the body.
- Those with damage to the nondominant hemisphere may lose not only motor function on the left side but their sense of body image, their sense of wholeness and the ability to put things together, their sense of art and music, their awareness of people to one side of them in a hemianopia or lateral neglect, and amusia or dysmusia.

Depressive illness, whether combined with dementia or as a separate disorder, affects every aspect of life and may well lead to suicide in older as well as younger people (Boxwell, 1988). We also know that depression occurs after a stroke, not only as a psychosocial response to disability and changed life circumstances, but as a biochemical outcome of the damage to the brain caused by the stroke (Robinson et al., 1985).

In all difficulties, the responses of the individuals affected depend on many factors such as personality, outlook on life, the extent of the damage to cognition, and the support given by others (Morris, Robinson, Raphael, & Bishop, 1991). Here, too, there are differences not only between professionals but between different families. Much depends on the qualities of previous relationships. Staff members readily criticize relatives who fail to visit frequently or who do not wish to care for the person at home after discharge, but this may be the result of the person having always been "difficult," having alienated those from whom support is now needed.

Study of textbooks, attendance at clinical presentations, and the cultivation of a sensitive eye and mind are the only ways in which we can equip ourselves to better understand the difficulties encountered by clients and their families in coping with acquired disability in later life. We also have to admit that patients are not always "easy" people. Therapy based on insight is often only associated with psychiatry, but difficulties with interpersonal relationships can occur in any population when we work with those in distress. The fact that someone has an acquired disability does not immediately turn the person into a plaster saint. Many of our clients and patients have been difficult people in the past, and it is rare for their new dependency to improve matters.

Exceptions are those who have been difficult because their dependency needs were not met, who "enjoy" ill health, and embrace the sick role in life. Paradoxically, they may prove difficult when we encourage independence or talk about the improvements we have seen. If we tell such a person that he or she has improved, we may meet with a response implying we have been cruel and unfeeling or that we are stupid to have failed to notice how disabled they are and how far from discharge!

Our only protection in complex, painful experiences of transference, hostility, and other interpersonal difficulties is to try to understand what is happening at this moment, what has happened in the past to lead up to such difficulties and above all, to understand ourselves and our reactions.

In all situations of loneliness, fear, sadness, confusion, anger, and so on, the music therapist has something to offer, whether in general support or in music therapy for grief resolution as such, whether we work with a young person in an acute hospital, an older person in a long-stay unit, someone with a single or a multiple diagnosis, with the family alone, or with family together with the client.

Deciding Which Approach to Use

Music therapists may need to put aside their usual patterns of working and use different approaches:

- Improvisation may or may not be the way to go. In the last stages of dementia, the strangeness of the music can confuse someone whose cognitive function is impaired, but familiar music helps to build bridges of communication.

- For some people, reflective improvisation brings, at any age, a sense of validation and a stimulus to visualization. However, it is important to gauge the style of improvisation to meet the client's needs. Strongly atonal or polytonal music does not suit everyone, and fairly conventional diatonic music may be more conducive to trust and exploration, whether the work is reflective or shared.
- For others, especially when there is a cognitive impairment, songs from the person's own past or composition of songs by therapist and client together with conversation, if still possible, may achieve trust more readily.
- Deciding *not* to talk to people, using only music, is generally inappropriate if we work with middle-aged or older people, particularly those whose experience of music is limited to popular musicals and films or ballroom dancing. Most older people are usually unfamiliar with nonverbal communication and may feel uncomfortable or even rejected by the therapist who does not converse.
- The person with advanced dementia in whom all speech has been lost, can benefit from familiar music combined with touch and simple comments such as "I think you'll know this song!"—to which no reply is needed.
- But the therapist who talks too much is equally unhelpful! It is better to listen and say little apart from making open-ended statements that enhance conversation, occasionally asking a gentle question.

We need to recognize feelings of guilt sometimes experienced by those who become disabled and by parents of a child who is born with an impairment or abnormality. Although generally physical illness does not elicit stigmatization, there are those (often older people) whose upbringing leads them to believe that any disaster is their own fault—so we see overwhelming emotional responses even in such conditions as stroke, amputation, Parkinson's disease, Alzheimer's disease, and other disorders of organic origin.

Stigma relating to physical disability is inherent in some cultures; a woman of Middle Eastern origin was blamed entirely for her baby son's disability at birth, was divorced by her husband, and was deprived of her child. Primitive groups that lead a nomadic life may also need to reject disabled children or adults, which rejection relates to stigma (Glascock, 1990, pp. 43–56).

Working in long-term disability with people of any age does not necessitate the development of totally different approaches in spinal injuries, head injuries, strokes, multiple sclerosis, or other long-term conditions. To that end, we need to

- be aware of differences in musical taste;
- build up a repertoire of music to meet the needs of the particular populations we serve, whatever their age;

- build our resources (multicultural and other songbooks of all eras as well as books of classical music) from which people can choose;
- become sensitive to people's feelings about playing instruments, singing, listening to songs of various types, and disclosing their inner feelings in music or conversation.

There are no stereotypes as to what age particular events occur. We do need to develop clear understanding of the particular disabilities we expect to see in any given unit, whether these are difficulties such as cerebrovascular accidents, Parkinson's disease, dementing illnesses, multiple sclerosis, childhood multiple disabilities, or any other difficulties that bring people into the health system or community care. With empathy, determination, creativity, knowledge, capacity for working in a team, and the ability to put all these together, we shall find that work in long-term disabilities has special rewards, such as are unavailable to those therapists who see people only a few times during a brief hospital admission.

Chapter 9

Other Loss Situations

Aims and learning objectives of this chapter:

- *Extend our knowledge of the breadth of grief and loss experiences*
- *Expand our skills in dealing with unfamiliar situations*

Because this book is written for professional therapists, it has focused mainly upon the needs of people who are sufficiently unwell as a consequence of unresolved grief issues, that they have been referred to us for treatment in a hospital, clinic, formal community treatment center, or private practice. But much will depend upon the particular culture in which we work, whether people are referred for help, seek professional help on their own initiative, or tend to battle on in their own resources. These factors determine whether or not we are asked to help with grief resolution. The work with that population is therefore described in this book in chapter 5. But the same methods could well apply to people seen in community settings.

Another factor affecting provision of treatment is that there are griefs that are accepted as normal and seem to have been resolved without professional support or treatment, but that reemerge, still unresolved at a time of crisis, so that there is a cumulative effect. When this happens, we may sense that there are several layers of grief underneath the one for which help is sought, and it takes skill to elicit them, to help the client perceive the link and be willing to deal with things from the long-distant past. This chapter discusses losses of the past and the possible subsequent effects on everyday life as well as the factors that may diminish the individual's capacity to deal with loss—at the time it is experienced or in future experiences.

Self-Esteem and Self-Image

Loss is usually perceived as associated with datable events that changed the pattern of life, changed one's feelings about oneself, or changed one's coping mechanisms. But loss may also be lifelong, so that it seems part of the inherent personality and causes are rarely identified. In such instances, loss is better described as "failure ever to develop," and is commonly seen in low self-esteem. This may be identified as linked with low-level depression or with dysthymia, and it can destroy capacity for happy relationships and enjoyable working life.

We meet this tragic loss professionally, but we also meet it in everyday life. Most of us know someone who is a driven perfectionist, constantly working (often selflessly for others), who has difficulty coping with any large or small failure that damages the self-image. Such people should be seen as victims of past deprivation, probably early childhood. As a consequence they have grown to adulthood seeing themselves as unlovable—unworthy of love. This is similar to the feelings of worthlessness and guilt in people with depressive illness, but is also seen in the "well" population.

Whether we can support the individual to achieve change depends on our relationship, but if this is in any way professional, we may be able to help. Change is not readily achieved, because to acknowledge the need for change makes it necessary to acknowledge that mistakes were made. Total self-confidence is rarely achieved and has associated risks. But deep-seated self-mistrust needs to be addressed, if possible, and to become familiar with the OK Song (described in chapter 3) provides a useful start. This song is useful because it helps to counteract the guilty yearning for perfection that destroys healthy self-esteem.

Relationship Breakdown

The ending of relationships is now so common that the onlooker may think, "So what?" But to the individuals concerned, there are many adverse effects on everyday life and self-image, with self-blame often predominant.

The way the individual copes with the breakdown of a relationship will depend on many factors. These include the person's temperament and mental health, childhood experiences of relationship stability or instability, self-confidence or lack of it, sexuality and attitudes toward sexual relationships, and feelings of guilt about reasons for the breakdown or denial of any responsibility. They may depend on the amount of affection for the erstwhile partner, the amount of emotional investment in the relationship at the beginning, and the extent to which that investment has changed over time.

Many of these are lifelong characteristics or long-term memories of previous experiences, and none of us is free from the effects of these, however well we think we have dealt with the past. When another loss is experienced later in life, even if the quality is only slightly similar, the effects upon the person are cumulative. Thus someone who recalls family misery and hopelessness when his mother walked out of the family has a double whammy when his wife walks out of his life.

Damaging comments made at the time of an earlier broken engagement are recalled if a subsequent marriage or live-in partnership comes to an end. There are endless possibilities, and even the most gifted therapist cannot be entirely certain what lies behind the response we see. But it is rare that a major relationship loss in adult life is entirely free from some baggage left behind from previous experiences.

Loss of Employment

The individual who loses his job at a time when other people from the same company are losing theirs has some measure of support in shared anger, is able to feel the loss is not his own fault, and may find support from a trade union, but this does not necessarily solve all difficulties. The person who is the only individual to be "down sized" or "sacked" is almost unavoidably left with personal fears and loss of self-esteem, however much this is hidden by rational explanations. The priority of fears will depend on the person's self-esteem and temperament, the state of current relationships, and past experiences of security and stability. With unemployment as with other losses, large or small, we are aware that early memories multiply the effect of later experiences.

It is one of the tragedies of our time that people's worth is generally assessed by what they *do* and what they *have* rather than by what they *are,* so that the unemployed person risks being seen as no longer of value. It is this same false assessment of worth that leads to stigmatization of persons with disability—they cannot do the things that society regards as normal, or they do them differently. In old age it can lead to feelings of uselessness, of being a burden, and ultimately sets the scene for so-called "voluntary" euthanasia.

Bereavement

Attitudes and responses to bereavement have varied over time, and there are still cultural differences. In Elizabethan England, it was normal for a churchyard monument to list the names of several children who died in infancy, and in some parts of today's world so many children die that they have no memorial—death in childhood is quasi-normal. One assumes the mother grieves for her loss but perhaps without the shock and disbelief that greets childhood death in the developed world. Although we see childhood deaths on our television screens from telecasts originating in third-world countries, untimely death in our own family and locality still saddens and shocks us.

But in our professional work we may meet people whose experience differs from our own, such as political refugees and migrants, who have seen death as commonplace. Yet the trauma may still be there. In those places where refugees are given a new life, we meet people who suffer the aftereffects of cruelty and oppression and who may respond to illness, death, and medical treatment in ways that are difficult for us to understand.

An interesting and challenging variant of the aftereffects of trauma is seen in second-generation survivors of the Holocaust, who may show symptoms similar to post-traumatic stress disorder (Almagor & Leon, 1989). In such a situation we work with the needs of the individual, trying to understand the particular components of the associated loss. For some people with whom I have worked it is linked with family survival and integrity.

For those of us who work with refugees and the victims of oppression, we equip ourselves as best we can by attending courses, reading appropriate journals, and finding out available resources for training and referral of clients. We also need to be aware of the differences in cultural background that may complicate responses to already difficult situations.

There are also microcultural influences in response to bereavement so that, as we know, some families have a tradition of stoicism; stoicism is also mandatory in wartime, when the ability of armed forces to "carry on regardless" is essential, and grief that has been put on hold may prove difficult to deal with later on. The same is true of some survivors of cruel imprisonment such as concentration camps. I have been told by survivors, that in such a situation, to show grief and distress was seen as a "win" for the oppressor so that stoicism in the face of cruelty became a form of victory. These past experiences, apparently dealt with long since, can affect loss situations encountered later in life.

The elderly lady who lost almost all her family in Dachau had her sadness made worse when her only grandson died. Her hopes for family survival had rested on the boy's shoulders and with his death, the family came to an end. Her anger with everyone around her, but especially with doctors and other staff who were treating her arthritis, had to be seen as displacement of her angry grief, which had its origins in events of fifty-five years before. The physiotherapist treating her was able to make the connection and referred her for music therapy, but early dementia combined with the long-held anger, fear, and sadness made it impossible for me to do anything except empathize with her loss.

This was not without value, but we had hoped she might be able to leave behind some of her present anger over her grandson's death. Her anger extended to her son for not forcing doctors to do more for the child, despite the fact that the condition was irremediable. The anger distorted what had previously been a supportive relationship at a time when she most needed support to cope with her disability.

Spiritual beliefs, religious faith and practice also affect our response to bereavement. Although we grieve for the loss of someone who was loved because that person is no longer part of our lives, our ongoing feelings can be influenced by our thoughts on the afterlife, judgment, survival of the spirit, retribution and reward, and so on.

Disabilities

When someone suffers a major loss, the response can be made worse by past experiences relating to a disability—whether one's own or those of a significant person in one's life. In such situations the disability is not the reason for the referral but is below the surface as a complicating factor. For example, someone diagnosed with diabetes, who has memories of another family member's restricted life and acquired disabilities resulting from the condition may have a catastrophic response to his or her own diagnosis. Someone to whom diabetes is unknown territory may be more willing to accept reassurances from the physician about treatment and prevention of pathology.

With some clients, one finds that fears may relate to general concepts of disability or a sense of imperfection and not to a specific remembered disability. Some, usually those with depression or dysthymia, see an acquired disability as a punishment for personal failings and may well benefit from counseling on a spiritual basis in addition to medical management of the depression. Other depressed people who have an established pattern of coping with their depression by keeping life under a tight rein, are so emotionally shattered by the loss of control their disability causes they become suicidal. Music therapists are in a good position to detect suicidality even in people who present a smiling face.

Some disabilities seem to carry more stigma than others, and stigma is in itself an additional source of grief. For example, the difficulties experienced by an older adult who is blind from macular degeneration tend to elicit empathy and assistance, whereas the older person who has become very deaf and perhaps has difficulty in adapting to hearing aids is frequently seen as a nuisance. We also see the stigma attaching to a family when a child is born with mental retardation, and the grief may extend beyond the parents when the abnormality affects marriage prospects for other family members. Parents who know the problem has its origin in a genetic defect, and there are many such conditions (Thaper, Gottesman, Owen, O'Donovan, & McGuffin, 1994), suffer from guilty feelings in addition to grief. We see, too, the bewildered sadness and anxiety of families who do not know how retardation or other abnormality arose.

It is important music therapists involved in grief resolution are aware that

- responses to present difficulties may have their origins in past experiences;
- these experiences may have been or may still be perceived as being of minor importance, and the person believes that the past has been dealt with adequately;
- these links with the past are not always obvious but may be present as "difficult" social behavior, passive-aggressive musical behavior, failure of cooperation, depression, and so on;
- those who appear to be happy, hopeful, and making a good adjustment are not necessarily okay inside;

- failure to benefit from therapy in any modality may arise from inner disquiet and not from obstinacy or apathy;
- after a stroke, depression may be of biochemical origin (Robinson et al., 1985).

Music therapy permits and facilitates both the disclosure of the past without fear of condemnation and some measure of resolution. This in turn allows the person to deal with the present without being held back in life by the additional burden of the past.

Losses

Losses can be described in an extensive continuum, so an event that affects one person disastrously may be of minor importance to another. An important issue may be catastrophic to one individual, but despite its importance, the same issue is dealt with relatively quickly and painlessly by someone else.

The factors that influence our response to a loss are various and include

- the quality of emotional attachment to the thing or person lost;
- the extent to which our self-esteem was invested in the thing or person lost;
- our past experiences of loss and how effectively and empathically we were supported in dealing with these;
- our inner attitudes to life and relationships;
- present attitudes of others to the loss being experienced.

The grief of which we become aware in music therapy is often hidden under a smiling exterior. We may have met a person in recreational music, rather than as a referral to us. What do we do in such a situation? If the person is already in a health facility where grief issues are dealt with, the answer is easy: we contact the appropriate professional, describe what we have observed, and ask that a referral be written for music therapy with a view to resolving grief issues. Our only decision is how to present our change of focus to the individual concerned.

But if we meet the person in a community music group, what then? If we believe that person may welcome the opportunity to talk, then some private comments such as these may be worthwhile: "I had the feeling that the song I played at our last session really stirred you up," or "Music can press all kinds of buttons for us, can't it, and sometimes we need to cry or feel sad over something that has happened," or "Some of my work is actually in helping people deal with their sadness when something has gone wrong, so if you think it would be helpful to spend some time with me, I could set aside half an hour at the end of lunchtime today."

This type of comment, spoken in as nonthreatening a way as possible, has proven helpful. Some people accept immediately, but some say, "I'll think about it," and then at the next session say, "You know what we were talking about last time? Well, I think I would like to come and talk to you." Even those who never accept an individual session can benefit from that initial empathic approach that indicated that it is okay to be stirred up by music.

Grief varies in its intensity and in the way people experience it, and we must never assume that we know all about it. We don't! But it is important to know that events and losses that society as a whole sees as minor can be important for those who experience them. Music therapy can help!

Chapter 10

Music Therapy and Counseling in Private Practice

Aims and learning objectives of this chapter:

- *Discuss benefits and hazards of work outside the institution*
- *Discuss methods that are especially appropriate to private practice*
- *Consider our own responses to difficult clients and the need for supervision*

People we see in private practice are usually less disturbed than those we see in the hospital. Although they are experiencing sufficient difficulties to seek help, they are not obviously psychotic or openly suicidal. But, even in private practice, suicidality may be hidden below the surface.

The criteria for seeking help, and the willingness to do so, are different in different cultures. In Australia, for example, it is relatively uncommon for someone to be in therapy or see a psychotherapist unless there are major problems to be dealt with. From my reading and observations it appears to be more common in the United States.

Who fares better, the person who manages minor problems alone and only seeks help when things become unmanageable, or the person who looks for help before matters become serious? No answer can be given, but the difference in culture will probably become obvious through this chapter—although I hope ideas expressed here will be useful whatever the prevailing attitude to the need for and the frequency of private consultations.

Referrals

The griefs with which we are asked to deal in private practice vary as widely as in hospital work: bereavement, relationship breakdown or continuing family tensions, loss of employment, loss of hope, feelings of failure. These and other human dilemmas are found in everyday life in the community.

We may find that people come to see us by word-of-mouth recommendation, formal referral from other professionals, or because of our professional reputation. But whatever the reason for their arrival, our approach will be much the same. I find out from the referring professionals what their expectations are from music therapy. Sometimes it is thought that we provide music lessons as a hobby to take someone's mind off pressing problems, and although music lessons can have a beneficial effect, the therapeutic aims of our work must be understood by both the referring person and the client. It is unethical to undertake "pretext therapy," appearing to give music lessons while actually having a therapeutic intent. Usually the referring professional knows the aims and objectives of our work, and the information given about expectation is helpful. For example, a psychiatrist answered my query thus:

> Well, she has been depressed for a very long time, and I think her recent bereavement is only one more thing, so I am not expecting you to turn things around completely. But I would be interested to see how you go with her. I think that music therapy may help her to open up more readily than she does with me.

Or, from a community social worker:

> I gather than it is only very recently that he has been coping so poorly with life, and I know that his girlfriend recently walked out on him. This probably made his drinking worse, so you may find you only need a few sessions to start him on the right track, perhaps persuade him to go to AA.

Or, from a family doctor:

> He has been very down since his wife died recently after only a short illness, and you may be able to help him get over it more quickly.

(In fact his situation was far more complex than his doctor realized.)

The Consulting Room

As music therapists, we need to have musical instruments readily available, even if some of them are not actually visible as one enters the room. We want the room to be comfortable and inviting.

- I have two small armchairs, not the sort you sink into and have difficulty getting out of, but only a little lower than ordinary dining chair height. These are almost, but not quite facing each other, so if the client wishes to avoid eye contact at any point in the interaction it is not difficult to do so. The chairs are placed with a couple of meters in between, so I do not invade the client's personal space. (The amount of space needed varies from one person to another.) A third chair is not far away—for me to use unobtrusively if empty-chair methods are required.

- Beside each chair is a small table. On my table stands a glass of water, a writing folder with pen, and a scribbling pad of plain paper; on the client's table, a glass of water, a box of tissues, and a few flowers in a small vase.
- There are two pictures on the wall. One is an open bright landscape with hills, valleys, cattle, trees, and fences. The other is a darker bush scene with a track winding into the distance between the big gum trees. On a table nearby, there is a small unframed oil painting of a seaside scene, with low bushes and a few large trees behind the wide curve of the beach where small waves are breaking on the sand. (See "Assessment Tools Not Used in These Examples," chapter 1.)
- The piano is against the wall, but in such a position that it is easy for me to look at the client whose chair is to one side of this while playing.
- A whiteboard stands on an easel a short distance from the chairs, with pens of several different colors on the rack.
- Some drums (bongos and a pair of Indian ceramic pot drums) and an Autoharp are on top of a nearby cupboard.

Welcoming the Client

Perhaps it seems unnecessary to describe how I personally do this because each of us has a personal style. Clearly our first needs are to have name, address, contact telephone/fax/e-mail numbers, perhaps the name of a significant other, but always the name of the person's usual family medical practitioner. This last is necessary information in case plans for self-harm are disclosed (or, less likely, plans to harm others), when our Duty of Care obliges us to warn an appropriate person. In asking for the last item of information, my custom is to say something like this:

> I always make a practice of asking for the name of each person's GP.[1] If I find that someone needs more expert help than I am able to give, perhaps they feel that life is no longer worth living, then I have to make sure they get help. I hope you won't be worried by this. It is just a formality, and of course I would tell you if I did decide to contact your own doctor.

So far I have not had anyone refuse to give this information, the emphasis on the routine nature of the enquiry probably defuses the situation. But for ethical reasons, I would not see someone who refused steadfastly to give this information, because of the Duty of Care regarding risk of self-harm or harm to others.

Formality or Informality?

Early in the first session I ask how the person likes to be addressed. Nicknames are sometimes liked because they are reminders of affection, but sometimes disliked because they are reminders of teasing and bullying.

Similarly with First Peoples: does the client wish to be called by his Western name or by his tribal name? An Australian Aborigine grieving for the loss of his culture, needed at first to be called by the tribal name given at birth but later, as he dealt with some of the worst of his grief, changed to wanting his white-man name, by which he was known at school and in employment.

But, as well as the name by which someone wishes to be called, there are a few other points I believe should be included in our initial conversation, if not already dealt with.

- Cultural factors: the language usually spoken by the client will probably be obvious, but the language spoken at home by client and family may also be significant. In some migrant or refugee families, the breadwinner speaks the language of the new homeland but other family members do not. Concepts of grief and loss may be strongly influenced by cultural differences, and these differences are sometimes symbolized by acceptance or rejection of the language of the new homeland. Of these we must be acutely aware lest our work conflicts with traditional thinking on life, death, illness of mind and body, and so on.
- What is the client's expectation of what we shall be able to do?
- How is the client going to travel home? Will anyone be there for company, on the journey and at home? The answer to this will influence the depth in which we work.
- How many sessions will the client feel able to cope with? Presumably fees were discussed when the arrangements were made for the interview, but there may have been further thoughts since then.

How Can We Help?

The idea that people can gain understanding of their own behavior and motives, perceive the effects past experiences and relationships have on later life and a belief that such knowledge can lead to change, has a long and honorable history. This insight-based approach is the philosophical basis for some schools of music therapy. An insight-based approach in grief resolution can be helpful, provided the person has intact frontal-lobe function, so that insight is possible; intact memory, so the events of one session are recalled to use as the basis for subsequent sessions; is psychologically minded; and is capable of change.

For change to occur as a consequence of insight, the person needs to have sufficient personal resilience to achieve change and be able to make use of a good support network. Otherwise insight may only lead to further despair as the person realizes more fully the severity of the difficulties. In private practice it is especially important to know about a client's support network. In hospital work we can usually assume that support will be available if more help is needed after a music therapy session, but for someone living alone or sharing impersonal living accommodation with only personal resources to depend on, we need to be slower and gentler in our approach.

We also need to know what the client's experience of written music has been, whether there is a piano or other instrument at home, or whether the client is able to "hear music inside his or her own head" without an instrument. This will determine whether we can suggest songwriting as homework for the next session or whether writing a poem to set to music at a later session is all we can ask.

Vignettes

- David was recently bereaved. His wife had died from cancer after only a few weeks of illness so that the shock was still severe, as was his continuing disappointment that plans for retirement had been lost. His doctor referred him to me for music therapy for grief resolution. Observation of some hypervigilance and hyperacuity[2] in David's behavior alerted me to there being something else below the surface. After playing some of the songs they had shared together, I wondered what the worst thing was about missing his wife, and said "Sometimes it is not only the bereavement itself but some other loss that affects us...."

  What he told me, in slow, difficult, and broken sentences, was that he had suffered for many years from panic disorder and that his wife had been his support.[3] Her absence meant he was deprived not only of his beloved and loving spouse but of the person whose actual or telephoned presence enabled him to do a day's work, travel by crowded rush-hour train, use the elevators at work, shop, and generally lead a normal life.

  David found it comforting that I did not see him as stupid or childish. I was able to improvise music that reflected his own uncertainty and fears that were nevertheless disabling—although accepted in his mind as groundless—and then his wife's presence with him in her lifetime. It is the person's own recognition that the fears are groundless that separates panic disorder from delusional thinking.

  We talked first about his grief over bereavement, with additional familiar and improvised music, followed by empty-chair work in which he expressed his thanks to his wife for all she had done for him. Next David sat in the other chair and spoke for his late wife. "She" spoke of her sadness at having moved on before their hopes had been fulfilled and of her faith that he would be able to cope with life without her. The fact that this was included in the words David created on behalf of his wife convinced me that whether he recognized it or not, he would be able to deal with his panic without her, if given some coping strategies.

After achieving a sense of completeness in this part of our work, we moved on to start dealing with the panic disorder. Resolution of this problem was fivefold:

- Demonstrating rhythmic breathing exercises, done first to a live accompaniment of a song he knew, then to this same song which he associated with his wife's methods of helping him to cope sung inside his head and remembering her supportive comments
- Showing him how to use other techniques, such as looking at pictures on the wall to deflect his thoughts from his own panic, since social phobias are known to be a problem that responds better to cognitive-behavioral than to insight-based methods (Clark, et al., 1994)
- Suggesting that he ask his GP for a referral to Social Phobia Group, provided by one of the Sydney hospitals
- Giving him the telephone number of a 24-hour support service to which I am a professional adviser
- Arranging two follow-up visits, alerting telephone volunteers to possible calls, and writing a report to his GP on the outcome of my sessions with David

- Ann, a nurse attending a staff meeting at which I was speaking, stayed behind after the meeting ended. She hesitantly came up and asked about the comments I had made describing a patient who had long blocked her grief over the death of a baby and the saying of good-bye to the dead child through music. She asked whether I had time to take her through this experience because, although she felt she had left the sadness behind, she was still haunted by distressing memories of her dead baby and by feelings of incompleteness.

  As is my custom, I asked what music she would have sung to her child had he lived. I suggested she cradle her imagined child in her arms and sing. While not forgetting him, I encouraged her to let herself feel it was okay to let go of the pain and unwarranted guilt she felt over his failure to live. Because of the circumstances of the interview, I did not ask whether the death was due to genetic condition, accident, or illness, so used the phrase "failure to live" as being suitable for any of these.

I played the music for her. She sang and rocked her arms to-and-fro, crying softly. At the end she stood up and said, "As a nurse I thought I could cope with this alone, but I couldn't. Thank you." I have no idea what happened next, but my guess is that her newfound serenity remained with her. This approach is identical with that used for many other grieving women, both inside and outside hospital (Bright, 1999a).

Regarding David and Ann

There are some differences of opinion among those concerned with grief resolution as to the extent to which the survivor needs to separate from the deceased. If by "separation" we mean people should entirely forget the deceased and act as if that person had never existed, then this is clearly unhealthy. There are some therapists, however, who advocate the maintaining of strong bonds with the deceased (Klass, Silverman, & Nickman, 1996). This attitude accepts that the dead are never truly forgotten as long as there are people alive who remember them, whether personally or by repute, and that we should remain aware of our attachments.[4]

Some therapists perceive the cultural norms of some "primitive" peoples as appropriate to Western society—in which the dead are regarded as still interested in, even involved in, daily affairs, as described so vividly in the book *A Pattern of Islands* (Grimble, 1952, chap. 6). There are those who believe we should not discourage such attitudes and feelings, even among those living in what we usually call civilized society.

In bereavement therapy, however, there are difficulties when one tries to define precisely the dividing line between pathological and normal responses. My own view is that one should never enforce the idea of putting our "good" relationships with the dead totally into the forgotten past. One should be able to remember and talk about the deceased. And yet the possibility of constant yearning for and dependence upon the dead, by which involvement in ordinary living could become impossible, is worrying. Careful thought is needed as to how to achieve a balance between maintaining and severing bonds with the dead.

More Vignettes

- Elsie, in her early sixties, coming for private sessions, described her sadness about her difficulties in relationships with men. After she had talked for some minutes, music was improvised to symbolize feelings of sadness, confusion, anger, and yearning. Her own interest in music led to the early use of receptive improvisation in the session. The improvisation led initially to tears, which she explained were otherwise impossible to shed, and Elsie said that the reflective improvisation had expressed what she could not put into words for herself.

We went on to deeper discussion about her responses to men. These had marred her marriage, and it seemed had their origin in the inappropriate behavior of her late father when he met her again as a teenager, after a long period of separation from Elsie's mother. This behavior was not what is generally regarded as incest, in that there was no intromission or genital fondling, but consisted of sexually based heavy flirtation, which she found repulsive—yet perhaps flattering?

For this client, separation from the deceased was important. She was able to recognize that it was her father's own problems that led to his inappropriate behavior, that she had not encouraged him in any way, and that she had refused to accept further invitations when it became apparent he intended to continue behaving in the inappropriate manner described.

After music and further conversation, Elsie felt she could being finding solutions to past difficulties and her unrecognized ambivalence about attentions paid to her. In this, the validation and insight gained through improvised music were significant.

- Beverley, a teenager in conflict with her parents and experiencing strong sibling rivalry with an older sister, came for counseling through music therapy. She was deeply saddened by the tensions she was experiencing in family relationships. Her parents were keen for her to find help and arranged for contact to be made, but left Beverley herself to make the appointment.

  In the consulting room there is a jointed artist's figure, and I asked the girl to set the figure in the attitude that reflected her current emotions. This assessment approach is not always used, but on some occasions is informative to both therapist and client. Beverley set the figure with the head bowed, arms folded, and trunk leaning forward over bent knees.

  Two types of music were used during the session. Spiritual songs, well known to her from the youth church she attended, and improvised music at first symbolizing despair and anger, but gradually becoming more neutral and finally growing into a mood of increasing confidence. She joined with this after a few moments, playing a large bongo drum, so that the music represented recognition of sadness and conflict, but later the possibility of slowly moving on. This was my intention and hope, and Beverley shared in that perception as the minutes went by.

  Even in this first session, Beverley gained some insight into her family relationships with increased confidence in herself and greater willingness to talk things over at home. She also realized that her parents' encouragement of her coming for help indicated a warmer attitude toward herself than she had previously recognized, since it allowed her the freedom to speak of them in derogatory terms if she wished to do so. She still felt there was a barrier between her older sister and her, but decided this was a fairly normal part of life that she "could live with."

Before leaving, she was asked whether her feelings had changed enough to alter the posture of the wooden figure. She smiled and moved it so that it stood more upright. The arms, instead of folded protectively across the chest, were both pointing slightly upward.

This last interaction illustrates the value of not taking sides. If Beverley was to be able to cope with sibling rivalry and difficult family relationships, it was more helpful if she saw matters in a reasonably balanced way, and the encouragement her parents had given her to seek help, and their clear statement that they would not expect any feedback indicated they were more empathic to her needs than she had realized. It was important to help Beverley feel I was safe to talk to, that I would regard her input as confidential, and that I was not behaving as a bossy parent or an overbearing sister. The key to the outcome of this interaction lay in the fact that the conclusions reached were her own, not the fruit of any instructions from me.[5]

Possible Hazards in Private Practice

Although the actual hazard may be minimal or nonexistent, we run the risk, if we work totally alone, of a client coming with an ulterior motive of sexual assault or other violence. One cannot guard totally against this except by insisting on a formal referral from another professional, but this is not always appropriate as some people wish to come independently. Having someone within call, having in one's pocket or on one's belt some kind of self-defense device, or carrying an emergency call button or personal alarm can provide some protection.

A different risk is to the client. We must remember, in private work the client has to get home safely! Some, but not all, bring a friend to provide transport or company on the journey. But with those who travel alone, we take particular care that our work is not at such depth and intensity that their concentration on the homeward trip is impaired, leading to an accident of some kind.

We must also be deeply aware of suicide risk, and it is my invariable custom to ask questions that reveal the possibility of suicidal intentions or attitudes. Having earlier asked for the name of the person's family physician, I can alert that person to possible risks of self-harm or violence to another.

Because of the possible stress of our work and the consequent emotional risk to ourselves, professional supervision is essential for all who work in one-on-one music therapy, particularly in private practice. It is vitally important when we work alone or with those whose transference creates difficulties for us.

Detailed discussion of this will be found in texts that deal specifically with psychodynamic approaches (Gabbard's book has already been cited), but we need to be generally aware of risk indicators, in which our own comfort is adversely affected, since many of these can have their origin in the client's needs. Such indicators include

- feelings of incompetence and failure;
- dread of a client's arrival, being much too aware of how much time is still to go and longing for the time to pass more quickly;
- feeling that the client is attempting to create an atmosphere of erotic love, anger, or both;
- feeling that the client is trying to damage our self-esteem;
- seeing the client as trying to take control of the session, whether by erotic themes, anger, or other controling behavior.

Feeling a failure does not necessarily arise out of the client's needs and transference. It may be that a therapeutic alliance is not developing, that our own response to the client, based on our personal experiences and relationships, is getting in the way. When this happens, and if supervision does not empower us to deal with our own difficulties, it is advisable to ask another therapist to take over.

Dreading the client's arrival can arise from any of the factors listed here: dread of feeling a failure, dread of possible risks, and so on.

When the client appears to seek an erotic ambience, this is an indication of problems of intimacy, of sexual relationships or control. It is often difficult for the therapist to retain objectivity, especially if songwriting is included in the work, with the opportunities this gives of explicit sexuality. Even more confusing for the therapist are the love-hate feelings that frequently permeate sessions with those who have these problems. Supervision is essential for the therapist to remain objective in such situations.

Those who try to **destroy our self-esteem** are often suffering from personality disorder or borderline personality disorder. Awareness of this helps us remain objective and undamaged, but since each of us has times of being imperfect, the experience is painful.

When a patient is angry with us or tries to control our behavior, it is comforting to assume this is a consequence of transference. This is often so, but it may be that we *are* behaving unprofessionally—accepting phone calls during a session or arriving late without explanation or apology.

With the critical client, we risk responding instantly and defensively, rather than saying, "That is obviously very important for you," or something similar.

Experience of splitting in private practice may be between music therapist and GP or psychiatrist. It is difficult to cope with, and whether one is the favored or the unfavored therapist, needs open discussion with all concerned.

Separation at the End of a Session

Each session needs to diminish in tension over several minutes, with a positive summary of what has happened and observation of the client to determine fitness to travel. It is useful to have a fail-safe mechanism in place in case there has been an unexpectedly powerful response and the person will not be able to travel immediately.

One must also be able to give a crisis telephone number to private patients, not to give the feeling that they will be in such a mess afterward that they will need it, but to reassure them that they can get extra help "just in case." The phone number one provides may be one's own or that of a twenty-four-hour telephone support system such as The Samaritans (also called The Befrienders) in the United Kingdom, Grief Support in Sydney, Australia, another similar service in the patient's own locality, or the number of a community mental health crisis intervention team. The resource and information we provide depends on local circumstances. One is not always available when someone telephones for help, but it has been said that even the sound of the therapist's own voice on an answering machine message has a reassuring effect upon clients. The wording and the tone of voice used in our recorded messages are therefore important.

Summary

Private practice gives us some advantages by giving control of our own time and our own premises. The potential disadvantages are possible anxiety about income, an uncertain clientele, loss of interdisciplinary discussions about clients, loneliness, and lack of support with difficult or dangerous clients. We may lack access to a professional library and have to pay expensive subscriptions to the journals of our own and other professions, and research will be more difficult to organize.

The disadvantages for many music therapists are outweighed by the satisfaction of working from one's own office, free from interruptions when at a crucial point in an important interaction, and giving the more relaxed atmosphere of a comfortable office instead of a hospital consulting room. Even the finances may be less scary than they sound, so long as we have good financial advisers to help make decisions on sick leave, retirement income, and so on. Reimbursement and medical insurance remain a challenge (Tuttman, 1998), but the satisfaction of working independently of hospital routine may be more important. In private practice there is a strong prospect of our work being seen as an essential ingredient rather than merely the frosting on the cake!

Chapter 11

Research, Evaluation, and Writing

Aims and learning objectives of this chapter:

- *Consider the need for formal evaluation and research in our work*
- *Discuss the value and usefulness of various approaches*

Therapists are under pressure from many directions to prove the value of their work, to justify being regarded by other health professionals as competent professionals, and to be paid appropriately to do their work. Managed care, the insistence of taxpayers and insurance companies that money for health is wisely spent, and the expectations of colleagues all demand our accountability, ethically and financially.

Therapy that takes place with outpatients or in private practice may be especially in need of demonstrable outcome since it lacks some of the checks and balances inherent in hospital admissions and discharges. But, whether we work in a facility or in private practice, we ourselves also wish to verify that our approaches are effective, that we are working in the best way with any given client or patient, and we seek information as to how and where changes could be made to increase our effectiveness. In everyday work, we shall assess the effectiveness of our work by study of clinical notes (our own and of others) in files and by discussion with colleagues in case-review meetings and staff-room conversations.

We can also demonstrate to others the value of music therapy by those same clinical notes and case-review team meetings, by case-finding in group work, by contributing to Journal Club meetings, or in other ways. By these means, we shall help colleagues see music therapy not simply as recreational but as an effective means of treatment for grief situations and the depression that can result from unrecognized and unresolved grief. Evaluation by participant clients is also of value when there are sufficient responses to permit us to draw valid conclusions from the opinions expressed (Dye, 1994).

Challenges in Research

We all hope to demonstrate definitively that music therapy works, but there are difficulties when we work as members of a team because we often do not know for certain which intervention has been the most effective. It is extremely rare for music therapy to be the only intervention, and most of our clients are also having interactions with or receiving prescribed medication and treatment from one or more professionals.

In preparation for discharge or when we work in the community, our clients will also talk with their community case manager or community health worker.

The medication clients receive may be changed from time to time, and responses to this may produce improvements that seem to be in response to music therapy but that coincide with an altered drug regime or other factors, and the cause of improvement cannot be isolated.[1] Furthermore, improvements may simply be due to recovery by natural resilience and the passage of time. The idea of an unchanging regime is often fictional. Most of us have seen how a change in nursing staff in a hospital unit can affect a disturbed patient profoundly, for good or for bad, and patients' complex responses to change of therapist due to staff rotation have been discussed in the literature (DeChillo, Urquart, Leavy, Andrews, & Frances, 1988).

Yet it is difficult, perhaps impossible, to measure the precise effects of staff personalities when trying to identify which changes are due to music therapy and which are due to other factors. We know that some clients who are placed on a waiting list for treatment improve, although "waiting list" is generally perceived as a placebo (Crits-Christoph, 1992).

This list of confounding factors that may obscure cause and effect in research may sound negative and despairing, but it is actually realistic. To recognize these factors when we write about the research makes it more likely that music therapy interventions will be accepted by other disciplines than if we ignore the uncertainties, deny the possibility that some people get better anyway, or claim validity for flawed assessment or investigation.

Case conferences work better when all those present acknowledge the difficulty in proving the value of professional work in the behavioral sciences, and we must recognize this is not unique to music therapy. I have found greater acceptance from colleagues by acknowledging shared responsibility for improvement than by implying that it is *entirely* due to music therapy that the client is getting better! I believe that to acknowledge the difficulties in achieving certain proof in everyday work actually improves clinical team relationships because this acknowledgment rings true both in daily work and research.

We are not alone in feeling frustrated as we try to validate the effectiveness of music therapy. Psychiatrists, too, face continuing struggles as they try to demonstrate the practical and monetary worth of their work, and this is especially difficult for psychotherapists whose approaches require extended series of sessions. I found it encouraging to read some comments on the value and reliability of clinical judgments by the experienced clinician. Abrams, writing in 1997, encourages his readers to remember that "controlled trials do not have a monopoly of truth" (p. 23). Although this referred to electroconvulsive therapy, it is equally applicable to interventions in music therapy.

Writing about Clinical Work and Research

Diagnoses and Descriptions in Psychiatry

Differences in terminology and diagnosis are found in many areas of professional work. This is especially important in psychiatry because there are differences in wording and also significant differences in diagnostic criteria and understanding of various disorders around the world. It is helpful to study the similarities and differences between the categories in psychiatry as listed in the publication *Diagnostic and Statistical Manual of Mental Disorders,* Fourth Edition (APA, 1994) and the World Health Organization's book *The ICD-10 Classification of Mental and Behavioural Disorders* (WHO, 3rd printing, 1992). The World Health Organization's publication *International Classification of Impairment, Disability, and Handicap: A Manual of Classification According to the Consequences of Disease* is also helpful to music therapists when writing for international readers (WHO, 1980).

Even within one publication, *DSM-IV,* there are two sets of criteria for dysthymia; if we are writing about a person who is diagnosed as "dysthymic," whether as a precursor to full-blown depression or as a separate disorder, we must state whether the psychiatrist made the diagnosis on the basis of the list on page 349 or on page 718 of that publication and which criteria we accepted when writing about the case history. This does not imply that we are necessarily involved in diagnosis[2] but simply ensures that someone in another part of the world knows what disorder we are writing about.

For those who are interested in reading about this topic in more detail or writing for an international audience, I suggest the 1996 edition of the *Oxford Textbook of Psychiatry.* Its Table 9.4 illustrates differences in diagnostic categories for psychiatric illness as set out in *DSM-IV* and in *ICD10,* and Tables 9.5 and 9.6, the differences between these two publications in the diagnostic categories for various types of schizophrenia (Gelder et al., 1996, pp. 254–259).

Differences in Diagnoses and Prevalence in Gerontology

In writing for an international readership, we must remember that there are different rates of prevalence for particular disorders in different parts of the world, that it is not simply a matter of different methods of reaching a diagnosis. An interesting article on this topic was published in 1999 (Copeland et al.) in which prevalence rates for depression in Iceland were compared and contrasted with the rates found in Munich, Germany. Gorelick and colleagues wrote of the epidemiology of vascular dementia and Alzheimer's dementia in Chicago, Illinois, discussing baselines and frequency, and comparing the risk factors for white and African American older people (Gorelick et al., 1994). This article, which used the same diagnostic criteria for the two populations, highlights the marked differences between the prevalence of the two different types of dementia in different ethnic groups.

Differences in diagnostic criteria have important implications for research into music therapy for older people; the same person might be assessed as dementing in one country, but not in another. When writing for an international publication, we must identify the criteria used in describing the population with whom we work.

In Canada, the United States, and Australia, *DSM-IV* is commonly used, but the United Nations Classification of Disability *(ICD-10)* is generally used in Continental Europe and for some purposes in Australia. In Britain the usual tool for work with older people is the Cambridge Examination for Mental Disorders of the Elderly (CAMDEX).

Another matter to consider if we plan to write about dementia is the discussion about Lewy body dementia. Opinions vary greatly between different neurologists, both as to its very existence as a separate disorder and its prevalence. For example, one article states that Lewy body dementia is the second most common form of dementia after dementia of the Alzheimer type (Gomez-Tortosa et al, 1998) with distinct diagnostic features; but an editorial in the *British Journal of Psychiatry,* referring to dementia with Lewy bodies, DLB, commented: "whether these patients suffer from a variant of Alzheimer Dementia or have a distinct disorder is still debated" (Miller, 1997). In which case it is assumed that the Lewy bodies found in the brain at post mortem are adventitious and not a significant cause of the dementia.

There are reports of persons described as having DLB who experience visual hallucinations (Ballard, McLaren, & Morris, 2000), and they may for that reason be wrongly classified as "psychotic." Interestingly, changes shown in magnetic resonance imaging were reported in the brain of a man with Lewy body dementia while he was experiencing visual hallucinations that support a belief in an organic basis for these symptoms (Howard et al., 1997). While we do not need to be experts or even informed in depth on these matters, the articles remind us that we cannot speak or write glibly of dementia as if it were an invariable condition, we must recognize the wide differences of opinion that are found as to diagnosis, prevalence, and the stages of deterioration found in these complex disorders.

We may also feel confused by some uncertainty, still existing, in nosology; what was previously described as "multi-infarct dementia" (dementia resulting from several small strokes) is now, in *DSM-IV,* called "vascular dementia." Since the new naming is not yet fully accepted, it may be useful for music therapists who are writing for a wide readership to refer to the condition as "vascular dementia (dementia associated with multiple strokes)."

Uncertain meanings of words can cause confusion in our work and our writing. For example, the adjectives used in research to describe the emotional qualities of music must be clearly understood and defined before the format of any questionnaire is finalized. On one occasion I heard a research project described in which

- the terms *palliative* and *sedative* were used in a questionnaire to describe the emotional aspects of music as if their meanings were different from—even opposed to—each other;
- palliative music *was* defined as music that did not engage the listener—a questionable definition;
- on this basis, Gregorian chants were classified as "palliative," yet church music of any genre can arouse powerful emotions of various kinds, and because of personal associations, often engages the listener emotionally, whether in joy or anger.

The researchers themselves became aware of the confusion and realized that results were not valid, but not all researchers have such wisdom. The meaning assigned to emotionally loaded adjectives varies widely from one individual to another. If we are to use descriptive terms and ask subjects to complete a questionnaire in order to choose which word best describes the music heard, we must, before finalizing the questionnaire, do a preliminary pilot study to ensure that everyone means the same thing by the same word. (Bright, 1976). When doing research, reporting on it, and writing about our clinical work, we must try to use language that is universally comprehensible to validate the results of our research and make our descriptions accessible to a reader who is not a music therapist as well as to our peers.

Other Research Challenges

Even if our work is already well accepted by colleagues in other professions, research remains an attractive idea for therapists. For our own satisfaction and to improve our clinical skills, we want to know *why* something happens, *why* this or that treatment modality works for some but not for others, and *how* we can intervene more effectively in the lives of particularly difficult clients. As one becomes more established, one tries to work out how to set up an appropriate research project, demonstrating the effectiveness of music therapy in one's particular area of interest, with ethical approval by the facility's committees on ethics and research protocol.

The challenges are many, but to be aware of them ensures that our approach is rigorous rather than facile. There are many matters to be considered:

- **Ethical difficulties** challenge us if regulations in the workplace forbid videotaping or tape-recording of sessions.
- **Questionnaires** may be a solution in some situations if they can be administered by someone other than the therapist doing the work and if there is a proven interreliability of the various raters. Some research committees have regulations that forbid the therapist to also be the researcher and insist the questionnaires be administered by someone other than either the therapist or researcher.
- Research is costly: do we have the necessary **funding** to employ observers, people to administer questionnaires, and so on?
- What are the ethics of **using students for research subjects?** How does participation, or their refusal of this, impinge upon their actual or perceived relationships with the researcher if that person also examines them or assesses their clinical work? Professional associations have Codes of Ethics that provide guidelines on this.
- If we **pay people to take part in research**, does this invalidate the results? There are those who believe that paid subjects and volunteer subjects respond differently.
- Which **assessment or rating scale** should we use? We need to determine the reliability of our questionnaires and rating scales so we are certain the deductions we draw from the results are valid.

Our Assessment and Rating Tools

Decisions that we have to make regarding assessment and rating tools:

- It is appropriate, whenever possible, to use published, verified scales to measure changes achieved through music therapy because it is not required to demonstrate the validity of that scale, as it is if the scale is one's own creation. It is known that using unpublished and therefore unverified scales produces biased results in clinical research (Marshall et al., 2000).
- If we invent our own scales, there may be difficulties in inter-rater reliability and in demonstrating that the scale has validity. This does not apply to a self-assessment tool, which is inherently subjective, but it is helpful to compare a client's self-assessment with a team assessment to determine similarities and differences. We must be sure that any tool we devise is actually testing what it purports to test! An interesting parallel can be drawn with early "Intelligence Tests," which are now considered to have tested cultural norms and literacy rather than intelligence (Heim, 1987).

- If we use an accepted scale, is it culturally valid? We know that skewed figures on the prevalence of dementia result from the use of differing rating scales in different parts of the world (Erkinjuntti, Østbye, Steenhuis, & Hachinski, 1997). Cultural factors may well be the cause of this. Similar difficulties may arise with quality-of-life scales or other measurement tools that are vulnerable either to cultural issues or different attitudes by the professionals in different parts of the world. The Cohen-Mansfield scale is often used, but it is only one of many assessment scales for determining the level of dementia present in any individual (Cohen-Mansfield et al., 1996). Perhaps it is not essential that we know about these matters for work in a single geographical area, but when writing for an international readership or attending international conferences on aging, the knowledge is useful.[3]

Decisions that we have to make regarding which research design is appropriate for any given clinical field:

- If we want to have a **control group** to compare with the treatment group, how do we ensure that the control group is truly the equivalent of the treatment group? If they are not truly matched, then the value of the exercise is questionable, and it is better to use single case study.
- If we want to use a **placebo control group**, how does one do this with music therapy? Techniques used for evaluation and research into medication are generally inappropriate for music therapy research. It is easy, for instance, to provide tablets that appear identical but may or may not contain the ingredient under investigation. But if we want to use a double-blind method, it is hard to decide what constitutes a placebo regime in our own work. Subjects can hardly help knowing whether or not they are having music, and it can be difficult to establish a difference between music therapy *treatment* and music as a *placebo* nontreatment regime.
- Is the **technique appropriate to the population?** For example, if we wish to investigate musical preference, most young people will be able to keep the early items in mind and at the end, make a decision as to which was preferred. But with older people, we first need to assess memory status lest the results are meaningless. People with difficulties in concentration or memory chose the last-heard item rather than one they may have preferred.
- **Single-case-study research,** in which each individual is his own control, may be planned for music therapy research, but again we must be aware of confounding factors. The outcome can become blurred if the person receives multiple interventions from various professionals—in which case the beneficial changes observed may have been due to other circumstances, not to our work in music therapy.

- Not all research methods are appropriate to music therapy. A method used frequently in pharmacy trials is as follows:
  a. Provide treatment and observe changes
  b. Withdraw treatment and note to what extent changes were reversed
  c. Restore treatment and observe to what extent the changes seen in (a) were restored

  This is an appropriate method for evaluating medication when lifetime dependence on medication is acceptable. However, the method is generally unsuited to music therapy because the music therapist's goal is to facilitate lasting changes that will continue to benefit the client even when therapy has ceased, thus minimizing dependency. For a chronic population with lifelong needs for supportive music therapy, the ethics of even temporarily depriving those people of treatment in order to produce statistics are questionable.

- Last of all, we remember that there is a tendency to "get better" with or without treatment. Although it is satisfying to see improvements as having their origin in the music therapy sessions, it may be simply that the person was going to get better anyway, given good nutrition, social support, and "time out" from their problems in the family or at work.

Study of various texts on research is essential, whether we are drawn to a quantitative or to a qualitative/phenomenological approach in music therapy (Wheeler, 1995; Aldridge, 1996).

Vocabulary: Additional Thoughts on Being Understood

Being understood around the world has already been discussed. But our terminology is important. Each profession has its own jargon, which may or may not be understood by the outsider. The special meaning assigned to words in different contexts is potentially confusing when our work is transdisciplinary. One is reminded of Lewis Carroll's character Humpty Dumpty in *Through the Looking Glass,* who insisted on his right to use words as having the meaning he assigned to them. "When I use a word, it means what I choose it to mean—neither more nor less" (Carroll, 1872/1933, p. 114).

The way we describe the people with whom we "do" music therapy is something to be decided when we write for international readers. As was noted in the introduction, some terms have particular implications in different parts of society. The term *patient* is commonly used to describe people who are hospitalized for treatment, and *clients* is used for those seen in private practice who are generally not perceived as "ill." In some places in the world, the current fashionable term is *consumer,* intended to empower the individual.

There are those who perceive the word *patient,* even to describe those in the hospital, as patronizing and dictatorial, symbolizing the worst of the so-called "medical model." On the other hand, *client* may have associations with hairdressing and beauty salons, the legal profession, or—as in parts of Europe—prostitution![4] *Consumer* is also objectionable to some, who see it as linked with "doctor-shopping," in which someone goes from one practitioner to the other, trying to get the most comfortable diagnosis. This comment is not applicable to those who seek a second opinion for health matters of critical importance.

For this reason, I generally use the words *patient* and *client* more or less interchangeably, but I tend to use *patient* to refer to someone I have seen during an admission to hospital or who has come to the hospital for a specific appointment immediately after discharge, when classified as an "outpatient" in Australian terminology; and *client* for someone seen in private practice in the community. I also use *client* when discussing general approaches that are applicable to people inside or outside the hospital.

Political correctness in terminology also presents a challenge. An editorial in the *British Journal of Psychiatry* (Reid, 1997) bluntly condemned euphemisms to describe those conditions that have connotations of stigma. Two terms criticized by Reid are *mental handicap,* which may have connotations of "madness" in the mind of the general public, and *learning disability,* which Reid believes underplays the extent of the handicap in the person's life.

Challenging behavior is also cited as an example of what Reid describes as the "utmost ridiculousness" of political correctness, resulting in loss of accuracy and meaningless terminology. *Challenging* is commonly used as a euphemism for "client violence," so an article on how to deal with challenging behavior is probably about how to deal with the client who punches your nose when you unwisely invade his personal space!

I consistently use the term *mental retardation*[5] rather than *developmental disability* or *mental handicap.* This prevents confusion with autism, which together with Asperger's disorder (syndrome), Retts' disorder (syndrome), and disintegrative disorder is described in *DSM-IV* under the grouping "Pervasive Developmental Disorders." Although widely used in Britain, *mental handicap* is also open to confusion because it may be seen as applying equally to psychiatric disorders, since organic brain dysfunction is implicated in many of these (Buckley & Friedman, 2000).

Another reason for using *mental retardation* is that this term must be used when doing a literature search if one is to locate relevant material.

General Comments

Writing about our work, whether for local, national, or international readership, and giving papers locally, nationally, and internationally, all lead to wider dissemination of ideas that are worthwhile. This in turn gives opportunities for replication that tests the validity of our methods, our results, and our conclusions. Our clinical notes within the facility, our research, and the written or oral professional description of our work and research are all important to the growth and establishment of our profession, and they are worth doing with care!

Chapter 12

Putting It All Together
Being a Therapist

Aims and learning objectives of this chapter:

- *Integrate our personal attitudes and attributes so that our work may be more effective*
- *Summarize the value of music therapy in grief resolution as contributing to wholeness in the client and in society*

Wholeness in Ourselves

Putting things together involves linking our work and ourselves, if indeed they were ever separate. Our clinical work, our relationships with colleagues in the workplace, and our research are, in part at least, the fruit of our personalities, our experiences, and the outlook that led us to be therapists (Wheeler, 1999).

Our work in therapy is affected by

- the extent to which we are at ease with ourselves (Cox, 1988, p. xiv);
- a genuine altruism;
- our capacity for empathy with those in need;
- our desire to find out why things happen the way they do and how they might work better;
- a capacity to profit from personal experiences of all kinds, yet also the ability to put our own agendas and needs to one side in order to focus on the needs of others;
- our modes of thinking (lateral, direct, or whatever is appropriate at the time);
- our enthusiasm and creativity in music and other modalities;
- our capacity to cope with human tragedy as well as our own inadequacies and failures;

- our determination and ability to cope with delays and frustrations in order to carry things through, but to also bring a project to an end if we realize that it is leading nowhere or hand it over to another if this seems advisable.

To achieve the ideal situation in all these is impossible. Each one of us fails in one or more of these parameters from time to time, but the wise therapist recognizes his own personal own vulnerability and tries to avoid repetition.

Wholeness in Our Work

Throughout this book, emphasis has been placed on the wholeness of musical and verbal interventions in therapy. In one sense, therefore, we do not need to "put it together" because the two have never been separated. Although the number of minutes spent in each modality is by no means equal, all are of equal importance and none is a makeweight (Bright, 1999b).

The stages in the growing understanding and development of the approach were these:

- Release, expressivity, validation, and insight came primarily from the music.
- The therapist's insight into what was needed in music grew from words in the referral, words in discussion with colleagues, and the body language and words of the client.
- The words exchanged during sessions developed gradually from a need to verify what the music has meant to the client and how he or she could use it.
- The words also grew from the client's response to reflective improvised music and to significant music from the client's past experiences; from the therapeutic process, from the ideas exchanged, from the sketches that have been drawn; and from the feelings recognized and expressed as the interaction proceeded within the context of a therapeutic alliance.
- From this, more music developed in shared or individual improvisation through songwriting and the selection of a theme song.

This process is still effective today, and the cycle of music/words/music/words/music continues as therapy progresses. It is, however, essential that music therapy does not remain isolated from other aspects of the client's life. It may have provided a respite, a break from turmoil and confusion, but unless we can find ways of linking the therapeutic achievements with living *outside* the music room, music therapy will have no relevance to overall progress through the world, no effect on capacity to build relationships, cope with difficulties, or face the inescapable.

This integration will include interdisciplinary discussions and the writing of reports so that progress or failure in therapy is perceived as part of the total picture, and other clinicians are better-informed for the benefit of the client. This last is achieved by the writing of careful notes in the person's file, indicating the music used, progress achieved or a break in this, ideas for the immediate future, and so on.

Failure

We are not always successful in our work. Some patients sign themselves out of the hospital "against medical advice," as it says on the form they are required to sign, some go AWOL,[1] some people are "stuck" and changes do not happen, some are so unwell that change cannot take place, some get worse, some "bust" (obtain supplies of alcohol or illicit drugs), some die before our work has reached fulfillment, and some attempt or commit suicide.

But the *we* at the beginning of the sentence above is collective. Rarely are we alone in our feelings of failure because many people share in providing treatment, and although failure may be therapist-driven (through blaming, failing to establish an alliance, and so on [Mackenzie, 1988]), the music therapist's style of working is such that this antitherapeutic behavior would probably be unusual.

Nevertheless we do need to look into our relationships with the client or patient if things have gone wrong, look into issues of transference and countertransference, look back through our notes to see whether there was something we missed—not to increase guilt but to be alert in the future. One patient told me he was soon to be discharged and sang a song about "soon our troubles will be over." In fact he killed himself a few days afterward, and I am still uncertain as to whether his song was a warning I missed or whether his decision to die came later, when his discharge was delayed.

Suicide on the ward is a challenge to unity, and we all need support through what is often called debriefing. The topic of debriefing requires a book of its own, but it is enough to say that it must be done with utmost sensitivity. Rather than intense reliving of events, which may fix ever more firmly the feelings of powerlessness and horror associated with the trauma, this prolonging and exacerbating the aftereffects (see chapter 5, "Flooding for Treatment of Post-Traumatic Stress Disorder"), our debriefing techniques should, in my view, consist of reshaping the memories adaptively so that they become tolerable and stored in the brain in a less painful manner. Confidentiality is paramount in group debriefing, and it must never be a witch-hunt for blame. Participants must be able to describe the feelings they had, the fears that what they did or failed to do may in some way have contributed to the death, and any personal "buttons" that have been pressed with impunity. Gradually the safe atmosphere and the group's support can make the memories tolerable.

Following one death by suicide, I sat with a nurse who had also shared in the young man's care, and we spoke about him. Still in my garden is the plant his case manager gave me on the morning after his death, as we all met for debriefing. She said: "He loved you, Ruth, we love you and we love your work, and we want you to have this." Such sensitivity and kindness does much to defuse the shock and sadness of suicide and enhance a sense of team unity in difficult or tragic situations.

Failure is relative, and it's not always as serious as suicide. There are times when we feel our approach does not quite meet the needs of the patient or client. But can we adapt our approach to meet the client's needs and avoid the trauma of changing to another therapist, having to repeat a painful life story, and establishing a therapeutic alliance again? For me the answer has been to take several short courses, study seriously appropriate journals and textbooks, and on many occasions, observe the work of specialists. To watch films and educational videos and use educational tapes expands our understanding and can be a substitute for direct observation. By so doing, we establish knowledge and some competency in a range of approaches, we learn the philosophical rationale for each, and we gain acceptable practical skills in the techniques of each. We also recognize our limitations and see the applicability of various approaches.

Putting It Together: Our Colleagues and Ourselves

In several places in this book, mention has been made of the need to understand the colleagues with whom we work and ourselves, recognizing

- our own processes of transference and countertransference;
- our yearning for or our apparent indifference to personal success;
- our capacities for clear communication with clients and colleagues.

On many occasions we need to put our own ethical, moral standards to one side as we try to understand the lives of patients and clients whose behavior is unacceptable to us. We do not abandon our principles, but we must be able to "forget" them temporarily, to avoid giving any hint of judgment—difficult as this may be. In work with forensic patients or those whose behavior is destructive and antisocial, we are not required to change our ethical, moral stance. We accept that our clients do not necessarily share our position at this time. We make it clear that we are working toward change because of the risks to society *and to themselves* of their continuing in the same way as before. Work with forensic or antisocial clients is draining, and support for the therapist is essential.

Relationships with colleagues can be the key to productive work. In-service training sessions help educate nurses and medical staff about our work. But since staff rotation takes place quite frequently in some places, we may not be able to give sufficient seminars to keep pace with the alterations in staffing, and private conversation is necessary. It is helpful to have a brief printed summary of the aims, objectives, and working methods of music therapy in the unit to give to new staff members.

My own practice is this: if a new doctor walks into the session to take someone away, I stop the session immediately, even if in the middle of a song, and say, "Did you want to see someone?" This usually produces some apology and explanation, and I then ask whether the matter could wait for *however many* minutes remain in the session. If the answer is yes, then I promise to take the client to the doctor's office after the session. If the answer is no, I say, "Well, if it is *essential,*... okay, but I will come talk with you later about music therapy!" I make sure I take with me an information sheet, leaflets, or other publications. Eventually the word spreads to new staff members and the problem does not arise again, or if it does, then someone is only taken from the group after preliminary explanations, arrangements, and apologies.

Splitting: Nomenclature and Consequences

Although the word *splitting* is used in different ways by different people, in the context of hospital staff meetings and general conversation the term is commonly used to describe conflict or near-conflict between members of a clinical team. It is often over disagreement about the diagnosis or treatment of particular individuals. Relationships can be marred by splitting when antagonism is created between staff members as the result of a patient's psychopathology.

Although intentional splitting can occur, it can also occur unintentionally when a patient feels more accepted by one member of staff than by others and behaves differently with that professional, seeking approval. This behavior varies, but often consists of enlisting one therapist as an ally, perhaps by saying, "I will tell *you* this but you must not tell anyone else," or by describing the therapist to fellow patients as "the only one in this place who knows anything," or by making similar divisive comments. Gabbard's striking examples of how staff splitting occurs and the underlying feelings that permit splitting to occur are useful for all of us (1994, pp. 167–168).

Some patients use the mechanism as a result of a need that Wright described in her book on psychological adaptation to disability (1960, pp. 114–115) as an insatiable need for uniqueness and attention. Therapists who work in rehabilitation become both familiar with and frustrated by the patient who sabotages treatment by various means—including staff splitting—because getting better means the patient loses the concentrated individual attention given in rehabilitation.

Splitting by Intent

Other patients try to split staff as a means of experiencing power and one-upmanship or as a means of ensuring that the therapist likes them. (Efforts to establish personal relationships with the therapist by personal questions may warn us of an impending problem.) This is compatible with Wright's comment and typifies one aspect of avoidant behavior, in which people feel comfortable only if they are certain of being liked and thus attempt to win affection. But the two causes for attempted splitting are not incompatible!

If we are able to perceive splitting behavior of any kind as arising from the grief of long-unmet personal needs, we may cope with it more comfortably, even if difficult. But whatever the reason, as therapists we must recognize the behavior if we find ourselves the victims. The way to avoid being damaged by this situation is to

- feel secure within ourselves;
- establish a therapeutic alliance;
- present the patient's point of view to other staff with care and empathy;
- avoid being The Lone Champion;
- accept the value of work done by other clinicians;
- be willing to discuss the matter openly with others.

The bias toward an individual was discussed helpfully many years ago by Constantina Safilios-Rothschild, when describing the risks to staff unity of one therapist becoming the champion of an individual client or patient (1970, pp. 149–150). As I wrote some years later, the attitude "Well, he works well for *me!*" spells the death of the team spirit (Bright, 1986, p. 183).

The Personal Needs of Staff

Music therapy is effective and has much to offer whatever population is in question. But the very success of music therapy can create difficulties for us in relationships with other professionals. Colleagues who are personally secure can rejoice in the improvements seen in patients or clients, whatever the context those improvements occurred. However, those who have personal difficulties, who need success in order to maintain their own self-image, can feel threatened by the beneficial outcome that occurs so often in music therapy. Music therapists who need success—either for themselves or for their profession—also face potential problems because of the risk that they oversell the success of their own work and undervalue the part played by others. Such professionals are also at risk of becoming pawns for the patient who is a would-be splitter!

When working in various units for people with mental retardation and severe behavioral difficulties, I found it was important to speak to staff members, saying something to this effect whenever a particularly difficult or even dangerous resident behaved in an exemplary manner during a music therapy session: "It must be really difficult for you to see this patient being cooperative and positive in a music therapy group when you've had a real struggle to get him dressed without getting your shins kicked! But part of it is that he enjoys music, and in his view I'm not asking him to do anything he doesn't want to do, so it's easy for him to be good in music sessions. Also I am only here for an hour each week, whereas you're with him all the time, so the novelty effect has a lot to do with it."

To speak in this way from time to time does not discount the value of music therapy but it does acknowledge the hard task of nursing staff who care for aggressive, strongly built residents. It also shows that we are not self-satisfied or superior. I used this approach when a patient who had tried, with great violence, to kill a nurse in the morning, ended a peaceful and thoughtful music therapy session in the afternoon by saying, "I trust *you!*" and I suspected he might also say this about me to the nurse concerned!

It is salutary to realize that the type of splitting that puts staff unity at risk can actually take place only through staff imperfections. If each and every member of the clinical team were *completely* self-confident, *completely* free of self-doubt, rivalry, and the need for approval, then no splitting could occur. But being a therapist does not guarantee perfection. Each of us has some inadequacies within ourselves, and it is these that make relationship splitting possible between dedicated and competent professionals.

The Need for Consistency

Good communication also helps us to understand each other better. Therefore, writing in files is not only legally mandatory, but it contributes to teamwork. This and attendance at handover and case-review meetings ensure that the client or patient is not receiving mixed messages.

Imagine, for example, the emotional chaos that results if one professional is saying, "Forget about your problems from the past. Just think of the future," and another is saying, "The past is like an unexploded bomb waiting to explode. Unless you can work out how past events of your life have affected you, you can't move into the future with any confidence."

We shall never achieve total unanimity of therapeutic philosophy, but we can communicate with each other well enough to avoid obvious major problems. From time to time we may need to change our approach in order to avoid confusion to the patient. This can be difficult and often requires compromise following proper interdisciplinary consultations. A balance must be struck between therapists with differing opinions as to how therapy should proceed, for the client's benefit.

The Challenges of Private Practice

Our own support needs are met in different ways, depending on whether we work in a hospital or in private practice. In hospital work we know if the session brings to mind matters that cannot be dealt with immediately there will be colleagues to whom we can turn for support and discussion. In private practice this is not so, and we may have to drive home from the consulting room or travel to another client for a home visit with our concentration impaired. We may prefer to believe that one survives untouched by a difficult session, but this is not so![2]

Although there has been some emphasis on risks, the fact remains that private practice is very rewarding.[3] One spends time with people, free from major psychosis, who are sufficiently well to be leading more or less normal lives and are probably more open to change than those more gravely unwell in the hospital. Because our clients are leading their ordinary lives, there is more opportunity to work together, trying out new ways of thinking and feeling, unaffected by the necessarily abnormal closed and restrictive atmosphere of hospital life. There is usually greater capacity for insight also, although the support and attitudes of family and friends will influence the extent to which the client is truly able to make life changes.

The client's financial situation may be a deciding factor in the length of treatment possible, one may suffer disappointment if or when money runs out before the planned program is complete. Brief interventions may be required for financial rather than therapeutic reasons.

On Being a Therapist

Ethics and the Duty of Care

We need to understand the ethical foundation of therapy as set out in the Code of Ethics of our professional association and by the World Federation of Music Therapy—and we need to know this not merely in theory, but see the implications of ethical standards for therapeutic relationships. These implications affect work with both colleagues and patients. Among our ethical principles is that of the Duty of Care, our responsibility to the client, to his or her significant others, and to society, to prevent harm (Treadway, 1990).

Competence and Extension of Expertise

We need empathy in our relationships with colleagues and clients, but we also need personal support, through professional supervision as well as satisfying relationships and activities that may be unrelated to work. These contribute to our mental health and ensure that we do not feel guilty at taking time out for ourselves.

We shall also feel comfortable in our work if we do our best to achieve professional competence and knowledge both musically and therapeutically, making efforts to improve our knowledge and our clinical skills. No training course equips us for a lifetime as therapists because we ourselves change, because the world around us changes, and because our knowledge base is constantly expanding. Without being overcommitted to the fashionable and the trendy in our work, we need to consider new approaches and methods.

Keeping up-to-date with journals is useful, especially if our reading can include publications outside music therapy. Interdisciplinary Journal Clubs, common in larger institutions, provide a breadth of understanding and outlook as well as promoting clinical teamwork by shared discussion.

Managing Separation

Today we often speak of empowerment, and bringing therapy to an end may achieve this, avoiding dependency by the client and paternalism by the therapist. But in any therapy, empowerment can be a comfortable reason for separating from someone we find difficult. Separation from patients and clients thus demands preparation as we think through the best way of managing this, the needs of the client, our own needs, how much notice of separation to give, and other details.

Summary

Our general approach should reflect a professional attitude. We are more likely to build a collaborative alliance with our clients or patients if we are perceived as reliable, planning ahead for times of sessions and arriving on time for appointments.

Of course, the needs for relaxation and peace of mind are common to all aspects of music therapy, but they seem to be of particular importance for therapists who support those in grief because the clients' circumstances may have much in common with or "hook into" our own experiences. If we find ourselves too busy to take vacations or too involved to have friends and activities outside work, we are heading for trouble!

> Knowledge + Expertise + Empathy + Teamwork + Time off + Work-free relationships and activities = A competent, effective, optimistic, busy-but-relaxed, long-lasting music therapist!

Vaillant (1977, p. 15) reminds us that the terms *psychological* and *health* are inflammatory words, and that *health* is both metaphysical and a value judgment (p. 15). He also forces us to recognize the risk that in being completely objective we may be so intent on studying our client's problems that we obscure the person's humanity. Music therapists, by the very nature of their work, probably find it easier than some other professionals to focus on the humanity of their clients. But we must never grow complacent. We must retain our sensitivity to human need, setting judgment aside as we attempt to meet those needs.

Grief resolution through music requires a professional who is

- **M**usical
- **U**njudgmental
- **S**ensitive
- **I**nformed
- **C**reative

- **T**eamwork-minded
- **H**opeful
- **E**mpathic
- **R**eady-witted
- **A**daptable
- **P**unctual
- **I**ntuitive
- **S**killed
- **T**rustworthy

Epilogue

Death through Terrorism

In response to the tragedies associated with the terrorist attacks on the World Trade Center in New York City and the U.S. Pentagon in Washington, DC, September 11, 2001, I thought it appropriate to include a brief addendum. Issues of grief and loss have already been dealt with in some detail, but most counselors and therapists know that the aftereffects of these terrorist attacks will remain for years to come.

Likely Problems

1. The sudden severance of a relationship that includes unfinished business can be a burden to the survivor. This may be as simple as a wish that one had been able to say good-bye or "Thank you for what we shared together." More difficult for the survivor to deal with are feelings of regret and guilt, when the last meeting was marred by anger or a misunderstanding which can never be resolved.
2. There are particular difficulties for survivors when outsiders assume that the relationship with the deceased was uniformly happy and they offer condolences in a manner that shows they are unaware of hidden ambivalence and conflict, perhaps even plans for the ending of the relationship. In such circumstances, it is hard for the survivor to cope with the simple sympathy offered by the community, and therapists must avoid making wrong assumptions.
3. Mourning is made more difficult when there is a lack of information about how and when death occurred. The feelings of uncertainty and anger are similar to those that follow death by drowning, when no body is found, or death in wartime, when survivors are only told that the person is "missing and believed killed." There may be long-lasting fantasies of survival and return after many years.

4. Absence of the bodies of the dead prevents normal mourning processes from being completed.
5. Survivor guilt is common after any disaster, when those who escaped death by chance ask, "Why was I spared?" "Why did God make me miss that plane and not so-and-so?" "Why was I absent from the office that day and not another?" People who were telephoned by those who sped toward tragedy are left with memories that are probably both uplifting and tragic, and no outsider can ever fully understand how they feel about the events and the memories.
6. The emotional trauma of those involved in rescue and retrieval after a disaster like on September 11, 2001, as of the bereaved, will be resolved only with great difficulty.
7. Fears for the future are almost certainly universal, with personal, national, and global agendas.
8. For some there is spiritual suffering as to why the events occurred; others feel only anger. Conflict may arise between a yearning for understanding, peaceful negotiation, and forgiveness and a belief that retribution and punishment are needed.

Comments

In the circumstances described by the first four items, some are able to deal with these—to some extent—through empty-chair work, whether in a consulting room or by symbolic conversation. A symbolic farewell and resolution may take place at a location significant to the lost relationship, at a church or other place of spiritual significance, the graveside, or at the resting place of the urns given to the bereaved.

The gift to mourners of urns containing ashes retrieved from the destroyed World Trade Center buildings in October 2001 shows that the focus on the urn for the symbolic farewell is particularly appropriate, given that so little is known of the actual time and situation of the deaths.

In all bereavements, therapists should never take it for granted that the relationship has been perfect. To say, "You must miss him/her" locks the bereaved person into sadness, which is difficult if in fact the main emotion is one of relief that the relationship is ended. As I have written elsewhere, it is safer to say, "As we look back on a relationship, we remember many things, don't we? Some of them are good and some are not so good." This gives the client the freedom to acknowledge difficulties as well as joys. This is especially important when the death has been public, heroic, or horrifying. In such situations, expressions of sympathy are even more likely than usual to be received by those who are bereaved. The nature of the death can make it still more complex for the survivor of a conflict-laden relationship to acknowledge—even to himself—

there had been difficulties. This, in turn, adds to the survivor's guilt about unfinished business.

A Final Observation

As with so many difficult and painful memories, these recollections from September 2001 can never be erased.

All we can hope for is that they can be "put in the closet (cupboard)" so they are still there to be recalled at will, but not carried as a burden for every hour and every minute of every day.

The sudden ending of life and relationships can leave us with unfinished business from the past as well as the present. Dealing with tragedy should never be a slick one-off debriefing. It should include a trust-filled therapeutic relationship in which issues great and small can be adequately dealt with by client and therapist working together for whatever time is needed.

Notes

Introduction
Music Therapy for Grief: A Personal Viewpoint

1. "The bush" is an Australian term for wilderness, an uninhabited area, but it does not apply to deserts.
2. Balint comments that if this focus and intensity is successful, there is a sudden flash of understanding that unites the patient and the GP and is felt by both. For me this flash is a common experience—usually following the use of reflective improvised music. (See page 14.)
3. "Reflective improvisation" is a particular form of receptive improvisation in which the therapist reflects back to the client the emotions the therapist perceives as currently being hidden below the surface, and often unrecognized by the client. "Receptive improvisation" is *any* form of improvisation to which the client listens without active musical participation; it may symbolize such matters as hope for the future, a symbolic musical representation of emtions which have been openly disclosed, matters which have been discussed, and so on.
4. A commissurotomy is a procedure in which the band of tissue providing neurological communication between the hemispheres is severed.
5. A hemispherectomy is a procedure in which one hemisphere is surgically removed, usually for otherwise-intractable epilepsy.

Chapter 1
Referral and Assessment

1. My 1983 diary notes I had a lively conversation in Paris at the World Congress, sharing with Florence Tyson our common dislike of formal questionnaire lists of items that the therapist marks off in turn!

2. Picnic (horse) Races are important events in many Australian rural centers. People travel hundreds of miles by car or in their own planes, and there are social events in the evenings as well as socializing around the track.
3. I could have asked about these parodies, but this would probably have diverted the conversation into trivial matters, so the opening was ignored.
4. One square forward and then two steps sideways, or two forward followed by one sideways.
5. A colleague in my early days in psychiatry said, "If you come out of a session wondering who is mad—you or the patient—the person probably has thought disorder!"
6. A weekly interdisciplinary meeting over lunch, at which there is discussion (led in turn by registrars) of an article previously distributed and studied, dealing with various aspects of research, treatment, diagnosis, and so forth.
7. *Roundabout* or *merry-go-round* are the terms used in some parts of the world.
8. Alexithymia is defined as the inability to use words to express emotions.
9. So-called, in ironical humor, because they have sharp hooked thorns, from which—once one is caught—it is exceedingly difficult to break free!

Chapter 2
Meaning in Music: The Basis for Grief-Resolution Work

1. The title of the piece may inform the listener of the emotional content in a precomposed item.
2. The article on pitch that appears in *Groves Dictionary* (Grove, 1995 edition) is of interest in reminding us of the dangers of generalizations about how music is perceived.
3. At a teaching session in the United States in 1998, I played a harmonized scale progression, stopping on the dominant seventh chord instead of reaching completion on the tonic. I then asked the participants how many of them could tolerate it left thus and how many needed me to finish it. About 50 percent voted each way, so I repeated the scale, but ended it with the A minor chord, in an interrupted cadence, then closed the piano lid. The burst of laughter that followed represented a mixture of relief of tension and personal insight!
4. The word *projection* is used in psychodynamic psychiatry to indicate an unconscious identification between what is perceived (e.g., in artwork, inkblots, or music) and one's own unacceptable inner needs, as when a person who has repressed unmet sexual needs perceives sexual harassment in situations where there is none. But the term is also used to describe psychological tests that reveal both denied and repressed material, so that Thematic Apperception Tests, devised by Morgan and Murray in 1935 (later published in a manual [Murray, 1943]), are often described as Projection Tests.

5. There is a parallel here with the use of untitled, unfamiliar pictures of human activity, as in Thematic Apperception Tests, in which the subjects' interpretation arises from their motivation and life experiences (Murray, 1943).
6. According to Stige, *language game* is a term expressing the concept that meaning in language depends on actions and interactions in specific contexts. Meaning is thus not given but created through social use.
7. This is not necessarily so. Tcherepnin's piano pieces Bagatelles Opus 5, of which the first is a quick and cheerful composition using large numbers of parallel seconds, would not normally be perceived as symbolizing emotional disharmony but as humor. If, however, the piece was played very slowly, the perception of the emotional content would certainly be different.
8. A lower (sometimes "inverted") *mordent* (literally *bite*) is a common feature of music of the eighteenth and early nineteenth centuries. The main note is played, followed by the half step or whole step immediately below, and then the main note is repeated. Usually this is symbolized by printing above the staff and over the note a single zigzag with a vertical line through it. The two notes preceding the main note are normally played briskly.

Chapter 3
Methods, Techniques, and Protocols in Music Therapy for Grief

1. See further discussion of changing approaches in chapter 12, under the heading "Failure."
2. Readers who are unfamiliar with the concepts of these approaches are recommended to find texts that provide a précis of each, e.g., the *Oxford Textbook of Psychiatry;* see the bibliography at the end of this book.
3. See the Introduction.
4. To avoid the complexities of him/her, I shall refer to the client as "him" but most comments apply equally to men and women. When gender is significant, this is noted.
5. Ideas on the practicalities of improvisation and its emotional content appeared in chapter 2.
6. In integrated notes, all professionals write on the same pages chronologically in any given patient's file, with different colored stickers for each profession. Entries are noted with the time and the date. It is easy to read what other professionals have noted regarding their sessions with a patient.
7. The piano is in fact a percussion instrument—the strings are hit by the hammers—but *percussion instrument* here refers to drums, tambourines, bells, xylophones, or other items that the player is consciously aware of striking.
8. Aphonia is the loss of ability to express all sounds, usually from damage

to the brainstem, and dysarthria is difficulty with pronunciation. Neither necessarily involves dysphasia or aphasia (difficulty in thinking in words and/or speaking in words), although dysarthria is combined with dysphasia/aphasia in some strokes.

9. See also chapter 10, "Regarding David and Ann," for comments on continuing bonds with those who have died.

Chapter 4
Music Therapy for the Grief Associated with Death and Terminal Illness

1. Expressing thanks for shared happiness is relatively easy, but music is useful for this too!
2. Divorce is not unknown through blame of one parent by the other for responsibility for genetic defects.
3. Needs vary greatly from one person to another. Some wish to know the truth, however difficult, but others do not. One surgeon says to cancer patients for whom prognosis is poor: "Is there anything you want to know? If there is, I promise I will give you a truthful answer," thus allowing the patient to make the decision.

Chapter 5
Music and Grief Therapy in Psychiatry

1. Due to chromosome abnormality, a person with Klinefelter's syndrome may have some female bodily characteristics.
2. See also chapter 7.
3. In these randomized trials *debriefing* must be clearly defined and the process described.
4. For more information about the potential benefits and risks of debriefing, see *Psychological Debriefing* (Raphael & Wilson, 2000).
5. See chapter 7 for further discussion on dissociation.
6. Note that this is a different phenomenon from the splitting we talk about when a patient tries to divide a clinical team into factions. See chapter 12, "Splitting by Intent."
7. See "Assessment Tools Not Used in These Examples" in chapter 1.
8. See note 6 in chapter 1.
9. The road map technique is useful in situations other than psychiatry. For example, see chapter 7.
10. See chapter 3, "The Personal Theme Tune."

Chapter 6
Music Therapy in Psychiatry: Work with Forensic Patients

1. One is still "alone" with the patient therapeutically, despite the unobtrusive, protective presence of a nurse.
2. One could also include a visit to the graveside to express sorrow there, but I have felt this to be inappropriate and the risks unwarranted, despite having taken many nonforensic clients on such a visit.

Chapter 7
Music Therapy for Grief Resolution for Those Who Have Suffered Sexual Abuse

1. A formalized hand, the index finger pointing, is sometimes used on a wall to indicate the way to go.

Chapter 8
The Griefs of Disability and Long-Term Losses at All Ages

1. I used the melody of the song "Good Morning, Good Morning, We've Danced the Whole Night Through." The song is on page 183 in the *Ultimate Fake Book* mentioned in the bibliography.
2. Avoid asking, "Would you like to...?" because the person will not perceive it as an *enjoyable* process, but it may nevertheless be useful!
3. This comment is an interesting example of perception that was probably at variance with the actual words used. Almost certainly she was told, not to "*get rid* of him" but "Put him in a home, dear, and get on with your life."

Chapter 10
Music Therapy and Counseling in Private Practice

1. GP = General Practitioner; I use whatever term is commonly used to describe the family doctor, not a specialist.
2. Hyperacuity and hypervigilance: abnormal awareness of things heard and seen, indicated by behavior such as jumping at a trivial sound outside the room, constantly turning the head to look out the window to see whether anyone is looking in, and so on.
3. The supporter of someone suffering from panic disorder is sometimes called the phobic companion.

4. A "bond" with the dead sometimes constitutes "bondage," which precludes growth and change.
5. Although not described in any of these vignettes, the pictures on the wall are also used with many private clients to help projection and alert clients to their feelings about themselves.

Chapter 11
Research, Evaluation, and Writing

1. We may risk falling into the well-known fallacy *Post hoc, ergo propter hoc* (after this, therefore because of this).
2. However, as an active member of a clinical team, the music therapist may well be called upon to give an opinion, but without being the sole arbiter or decision maker about diagnosis.
3. See also comments on rating scales for agitation in older people, in chapter 8 under the heading "Skills Required and Tools Available."
4. I discovered this in Spain, upon seeing the astonished look on the interpreter's face when I spoke of music therapy with *clients;* she asked for clarification and explained the implications of the word for the students!
5. See comments on nomenclature (Bright, 1997b, p. 3).

Chapter 12
Putting It All Together: Being a Therapist

1. AWOL is the acronym for **A**bsent **W**ith**O**ut **L**eave.
2. When driving home from a consultation in which I had been given an equivocal verdict from a medical specialist, I had a minor road accident, not because my sight was impaired but because my concentration was. I had often said that driving was hazardous after a difficult therapy session but had not expected that I would provide practical evidence of this.
3. Private practice is rewarding in results of therapy, even if not financially!

References

Abrams, R. (1997). *Electroconvulsive therapy.* Oxford: Oxford University Press.

Adams, E. D., & Victor, M. (1993). *Principles of neurology.* New York: McGraw-Hill.

Aldridge, D. (1996). *Music Therapy Research and Practice in Medicine.* London: Jessica Kingsley.

Alexopoulos, G. S., Abrams, R. C., Young, R. C., & Shamoian, C. A. (1988). Cornell scale for depression in dementia. *Biological Psychiatry, 23*, 271–284.

Allen, J. G., Tarnoff, G., & Coyne, L. (1985). Therapeutic alliance and long-term hospital treatment outcome. *Comprehensive Psychiatry, 26*(2), 187–194.

Almagor, M., & Leon, G. R. (1989). Transgenerational effects of the concentration camp experience. In Marcus & Rosenburg (Eds.), *Psychotherapy with holocaust survivors* (pp. 185–196). New York: Praeger.

American Psychiatric Association. (1994). *Diagnostic and statistical manual of mental disorders* (4th ed.). Washington, DC: Author.

Atchison, A. C., & McFarlane, A. C. (1994). A review of dissociation and dissociative disorders. *Australian and New Zealand Journal of Psychiatry, 28*, 591–599.

Bachelor, A. (1991). Comparison and relationship to outcome of diverse dimensions of the helping alliance as seen by therapist and client. *Psychotherapy, 28*(4), 534–549.

Balint, M. (1964). *The doctor, his patient and the illness* (2nd ed.). London: Pitman Medical.

Balint, M., Ornstein, P. H., & Balint, E. (1982). *Focal psychotherapy.* London: Tavistock.

Ballard, C., McLaren, A., & Morris, C. (2000). Non-Alzheimer dementia. *Current Opinion in Psychiatry, 13,* 409–414.

Barber, J. P., Crits-Christoph, P., & Luborsky, L. (1996). Effects of therapist adherence and competence in patient outcome in brief dynamic therapy. *Journal of Consulting and Clinical Psychology, 64*(3), 619–622.

Bartlett, J. C. (1932/1995). *Remembering* (Vintage ed.). Cambridge, UK: Cambridge University Press.

Beats, B. (1996). Biological origin of depression in later life. *International Journal of Geriatric Psychiatry, 11,* 349–354.

Berne, E. (1960). *The games people play.* London: André Deutsch.

Boxwell, A. O. (1988). Geriatric suicide: The preventable death. *Nurse Practitioner, 13*(6), 10–19.

Bremner, J. D., Randall, P., Scott, T. M., Bronen, R. A., Seibyl, J. P., Southwick, S. M., Delaney, R. C., McCarthy, G., Charney, D. S., & Innis, R. B. (1995). MRI-based measurement of hippocampal volume in combat-related posttraumatic stress disorder. *American Journal of Psychiatry, 152*(7), 973–981.

Bright, R. (1975). Amusia: The lateralisation of music function and its possible significance in rehabilitation. *Proceedings of Australian Association of Gerontology, 2*(3), 145–149.

Bright, R. (1976). Perception of emotive content of unfamiliar music: A study of three populations. *Proceedings of Australian Music Therapy Association Conference.*

Bright, R. (1986). *Grieving: A handbook for those who care.* St. Louis, MO: MMB Music.

Bright, R. (1989). Music therapy and the brain-damaged alcoholic. In J. Shephard (Ed.), *Advances in behavioural medicine 6* (pp. 301–314). Sydney University, Cumberland College of Health Sciences.

Bright, R. (1993). Cultural influence in music therapy. In N. Heal & A. Wigram (Eds.), *Music therapy in health and education.* London: Jessica Kingsley.

Bright, R. (1994). Music therapy. In Chiu & Ames (Eds.), *Functional psychiatric disorders of the elderly* (chap. 34). Cambridge, UK: Cambridge University Press.

Bright, R. (1996). *Grief and powerlessness.* London: Jessica Kingsley.

Bright, R. (1997a). *Music therapy in the dementias: Improving the quality of life* (2nd ed.). St. Louis, MO: MMB Music.

Bright, R. (1997b). *Wholeness in later life.* London: Jessica Kingsley.

Bright, R. (1999a). *Looking back over 40 years of music therapy: The therapeutic alliance in supportive and eclectic music therapy.* Paper presented at the congress of World Federation of Music Therapy, Washington, DC.

Bright, R. (1999b, Fall). Music Therapy for Grief Resolution. *Bulletin of the Menninger Clinic, 63*(4), 481–498.

Bright, R., & Signorelli, R. (1999). Improving the quality of life in profoundly brain-impaired clients. The role of music therapy. *MusicMedicine 3* (pp. 254–263). Melbourne, Australia: University of Melbourne.

Brodaty, H. (1983). Techniques in brief psychotherapy. *Australia and New Zealand Journal of Psychiatry, 17*(2), 109–115.

Brogan, C. (2001). Long-term psychotherapeutic relationships in schizophrenia. *British Journal of Psychiatry, 178,* 478.

Bryer, J. B., Nelson, B. A., Miller, J. B., & Krol, B. A. (1987). Childhood sexual and physical abuse: A factor in adult psychiatric illness. *American Journal of Psychiatry, 144,* 1426–1430.

Buckley, P. F., & Friedman, C. (2000). Magnetic resonance spectroscopy: Bridging the neurochemistry and neuroanatomy of schizophrenia. (Editorial.) *British Journal of Psychiatry, 176,* 203–205.

Carroll, L. [Dodgson, C. L.] (1872/1933). *Through the looking glass.* London: Macmillan.

Chochinov, H. M., Wilson, K. G., Enns, M., & Lander, S. (1994). Prevalence of depression in the terminally ill: Effects of diagnostic criteria and symptom threshold judgements. *American Journal of Psychiatry, 151*(4), 537–540.

Chu, J. A., & Dill, D. L. (1991). Dissociation, borderline personality disorder and childhood trauma. *American Journal of Psychiatry, 148*(6), 812–813.

Clark, D. M., Salkovskis, P. M., Hackman, A., Middleton, H., Anastasiades, P., & Gelder, M. (1994). A comparison of cognitive therapy, applied relaxation and imipramine in the treatment of panic disorder. *British Journal of Psychiatry, 164,* 759–769.

Cohen-Mansfield, J., Reisberg, B., Bonnema, J., Berg, B., Dastoor, D. P., Pfeffer, R. I., & Cohen, G. D. (1996). Staging methods for the assessment of dementia: Perspectives. *Journal of Clinical Psychiatry, 57*(5), 190–198.

Copeland, J. R. M., Beekman, A. T. F., Dewey, M. E., Hooijer, C., Jordan, A., Lawlor, B. A., Linden, M., Lobo, A., Magnusson, H., Mann, A. H., Meller, I., Prince, M. J., Reischies, C., Turrina, C., deVries, M. W., & Wilson, K. C. M. (1999). Depression in Europe. *British Journal of Psychiatry, 194,* 312–321.

Cox, M. (1988). *Structuring the therapeutic process.* London: Jessica Kingsley.

Critchley, M. (1953). *The parietal lobes.* New York: Hafner Publications.

Crits-Christoph, P. (1992). The efficacy of brief dynamic psychotherapy. *American Journal of Psychiatry, 149,* 151–158.

DeChillo, N., Urquart, B., Leavy, A., Andrews, S., & Frances, A. (1988). Patients' reactions to therapist rotation. *Hospital and Community Psychiatry, 39*(3), 197–200.

De Jong, P., & Hopwood, L. E. (1996). Outcome research on treatment conducted at the Brief Family Therapy Center 1992–1993. In Miller, Hubble, & Duncan (Eds.), *Handbook of Solution-Focused Brief Therapy.* San Francisco: Jossey-Bass.

Doka, K. (1989). *Disenfranchised grief.* Lexington, MA: Lexington Books.

Dye, S. (1994). The issues surrounding the evaluation by clients of the impact of two music therapy programmes in an acute psychiatric setting. *Australian Journal of Music Therapy, 5,* 19–31.

Ellard, J. (1968). Emotional responses to death. *Medical Journal of Australia, 1*(23), 979–983.

Erdonmez Grocke, D. (1999). The music which underpins pivotal moments in guided imagery and music. In T. Wigram & J. de Backer (Eds.), *Clinical applications of music therapy in psychiatry* (pp. 197–210). London: Jessica Kingsley.

Erikson, N. G., & Lundin, T. (1996). Early traumatic stress reactions among Swedish survivors of the m/s Estonia disaster. *British Journal of Psychiatry, 169,* 713–716.

Erkinjuntti, T., Østbye, T., Steenhuis, R., & Hachinski, V. (1997). The effect of different diagnostic criteria on prevalence and dementia. *New England Journal of Medicine, 337,* 1667–1674.

Fava, G. A., Rafanelli, C., Cazzaro, M., Conti, S., & Grandi, S. (1998). Well-being therapy: A novel psychotherapeutic approach for the residual symptoms of affective disorders. *Psychological Medicine, 28,* 475–480.

Folstein, M. F., Folstein, S. E., & McHugh, P. B. (1975). "Mini-mental state": A practical method of grading the cognitive state of patients, for the clinician. *Journal of Psychiatric Research, 12,* 189–198.

Gabbard, G. O. (1994). *Psychodynamic psychiatry in clinical practice: The DSM-IV edition.* Washington, DC: American Psychiatric Press.

Galey, I. [Pseudonym] (1988). *I couldn't cry when daddy died.* Auckland, New Zealand: Benton Ross Press. (In USA, Racine, WI: Mother Courage Press.)

Gelder, M., Gath, D., Mayou, R., & Cowen, P. (Eds.). (1996). *The Oxford textbook of psychiatry.* Oxford: Oxford University Press.

Gieser, L., & Stein, M. L. (Eds.). (1999). *Evocative images: the thematic apperception test and the art of projection.* Washington, DC: American Psychological Association.

Giles, M., & Kraya, N. A. F. (1998). The murder of psychiatrists and other health professionals. *Australasian Psychiatry, 6*(3), 138–141.

Glascock, A. P. (1990). "By any other name, it is still killing": a comparison of the treatment of the elderly in America and other societies. In J. Sokalovsky (Ed.), *The Cultural Context of Aging.* New York: Bergin and Garvey.

Glaser, W. (1998). Psychiatry and paedophilia: A major public health issue. *Australia and New Zealand Journal of Psychiatry, 32,* 162–167.

Gomez-Tortosa, E., Ingraham, A. D., Irizarry, M. C., & Hyman, B. T. (1998). Dementia with Lewy bodies. *Journal American Geriatrics Society, 46,* 1449–1458.

Gorelick, P. B., Freels, S., Harris, Y., Dellear, T., Billingly, M., & Brown, N. (1994). Epidemiology of vascular and Alzheimer's dementia among African Americans in Chicago. *Neurology, 44,* 1391–1396.

Grimble, A. (1969). *A pattern of islands.* London: John Murray.

Grove, G. (1995). Pitch. In *New Grove dictionary of music and musicians* (paperback edition, Vol. 14, pp. 779–786). UK: McMillan.

Heim, A. W. (1987). Intelligence: Its assessment. In R. Gregory (Ed.), *The Oxford companion to the mind* (pp. 379–381). Oxford: Oxford University Press.

Hinton, J. (1967). *Dying.* Harmondsworth, UK: Penguin Books.

Hodkinson, H. M. (1972). Evaluation of a mental test score for assessment of mental impairment in the elderly. *Age & Ageing, 1,* 233–238.

Howard, R., David, A., Woodruff, P., Mellers, J., Wright, J., Brammer, M., Bullmore, E., & Williams, S. (1997). Seeing visual hallucinations with functional magnetic resonance imaging [Abstract]. *Dementia and Geriatric Cognitive Disorders, 8*(2), 73–77.

Iveson, C. (1994). Solution-focused brief therapy. *British Journal of Occupational Therapy, 57*(3), 95–98.

Kaplan, H. I., & Sadock, B. J. (Eds.). (1987). *Comprehensive textbook of psychiatry* (chap. 51). Baltimore and London: Williams and Wilkins.

Killick, E. J. (Ed). (1997). *You are words: Dementia poems* (especially p. 47). London, Hawker Publications Limited.

Kirkland, K. & McIlveen, H. (1999). Full circle: Spiritual therapy for people with dementia. *American Journal of Alzheimer's Disease, 14*(4), 245–247.

Kirkmayer, L. J., & Robbins, J. M. (1993). Cognitive and social correlates of the Toronto alexythymia scale. *Psychosomatics, 34,* 41–52.

Klass, D., Silverman, P. R., & Nickman, S. L. (1996). *Continuing bonds.* Bristol, UK: Taylor and Francis.

Knorring, L. von, Perris, C., Eisemann, M., Eriksson, L., & Perris, H. (1983). Pain as a symptom of depressive disorders. *Pain, 17,* 377–384.

Kopecky, H. J., & Yudofsky, S. C. (1999). Agitation: Conceptualisation, measurement and treatment. *Bulletin of the Menninger Clinic, 63*(2), (Suppl. A), A31–A52.

Krout, R. (1999). *Songs from sorrow, songs from joy.* St. Louis, MO: MMB Music.

Kubler Ross, E. (1974). *Questions and answers on death and dying.* New York: MacMillan Publishing.

Lafond, V. (1994). *Grieving mental illness: A guide for patients and their caregivers.* Toronto: University of Toronto Press.

Lewis, D. O., Yeager, C. A., Swica, Y., Pincus, J. H., & Lewis, M. (1997). Objective demonstration of child abuse and dissociation in 12 murderers with Dissociative Identity Disorder. *American Journal of Psychiatry, 154,* 1703–1710.

Lippman, S. B., James, W. A., & Frierson, R. L. (1993). AIDS and the family: Implications for counseling. *AIDS-CARE, 5*(1), 71–78.

MacCulloch, M. J. (1999). Eye movement desensitisation and reprocessing. *Advances in Psychiatric Treatment, 5,* 120–125.

Mackenzie, K. R. (1988). Recent developments in brief psychotherapy. *Hospital and Community Psychiatry, 39*(7), 742–752.

Malan, D. H. (1976). *The frontiers of brief psychotherapy.* New York: Plenum Publishing.

Mann, J. J., Waternaux, C., Haas, G. L., & Malone, K. (1999). Toward a clinical model of suicidal behavior in psychiatric patients. *American Journal of Psychiatry, 156*(2), 181–189.

Marshall, M., Lockwood, A., Bradley, C., Adams, C., Joy, C., & Fenton, M. (2000). Unpublished rating scales as a major source of bias in randomised trials of treatment. *British Journal of Psychiatry, 176,* 249–252.

Mead, M., & Bateson, G. (1962). *Balinese character.* New York: Academy of Science.

Miller, B. L. (1997). Editorial: Clinical advances in degenerative dementia. *British Journal of Psychiatry, 171,* 1–3.

Miller, B. L., Cummings, J. L., Prince, F., Ponton, M., & Cotman, C. (1998). Emergence of artistic talent in frontotemporal dementia. *Neurology, 51,* 978–981.

Miller, B. L., Boone, K., Cummings, J. L., Read, S. L., & Mishkin, F. (2000). Functional correlates and visual ability in frontotemporal dementia. *British Journal of Psychiatry, 176,* 458–467.

Miller, S. D., Hubble, M. A., & Duncan, B. L. (1996). *Handbook of solution-focused brief therapy.* San Francisco: Jossey-Bass.

Mollon, P. (1998). *Remembering trauma: A psychotherapist's guide to memory and illusion.* Chichester, UK: Wiley and Sons.

Morgan, C. D., & Murray, H. A. (1935). A method for investigating fantasies: The thematic apperception test. *Archives of Neurological Psychiatry, 34,* 289–306.

Morgan, H. G. (1994). How feasible is suicide prevention? *Current Opinion in Psychiatry, 7,* 111–118.

Morris, P. L. P., Robinson, R. G., Raphael, B., & Bishop, D. (1991). The relationship between the perception of social support and post-stroke depression in hospitalized patients. *Psychiatry, 54,* 306–315.

Mullen, P. C., Martin, J. L., Anderson, J. C., Romans, S. E., & Herbison, G. P. (1993). Childhood sexual abuse and mental health in adult life. *British Journal of Psychiatry, 163,* 721–732.

Munro, S. (1984). *Music therapy in palliative/hospice care.* St. Louis, MO: MMB Music.

Murray, H. A. (1943). *Thematic apperception test: Manual.* Cambridge, MA: Harvard College.

O'Callaghan, C. (1995). Lyrical analysis of songs written by palliative care patients [Abstract]. In *The Conference Collection* (pp. 41–43). Turramurra, NSW: Australian Music Therapy Association.

Palmer, R. L., Chaloner, D. A., & Oppenheimer, R. (1992). Childhood sexual experiences with adults reported by female psychiatric patients. *British Journal of Psychiatry, 160,* 261–265.

Palmer, R. L., Oppenheimer, R., Dignon, A., Chaloner, D. A., & Howells, K. (1990). Childhood sexual experiences with adults reported by women with eating disorders: An extended series. *British Journal of Psychiatry, 156,* 699–703.

Parker, G. (1999). Bipolar disorder: The latest. *Australian Doctor, 20,* 49.

Persad, E., Oluboka, O. J., Sharma, V., Mazmanian, D., & Kuenoman, K. (1996). The phenomenon of rapid cycling in bipolar mood disorder. *Canadian Journal of Psychiatry, 41,* 23–27.

Phillips, J. B. (1986). *Your God is too small.* New York: Phoenix Press/Walker and Co.

Phillips, K. A. (1998, Fall). Body dysmorphic disorder: Clinical aspects and treatment strategies. *Bulletin of the Menninger Clinic,* (Suppl. A), A33–A45.

Pitt, B. (1994). Medical co-morbidity: Presentation in a general hospital setting. In E. Chiu & D. Amers (Eds.), *Functional psychiatric disorders of the elderly* (pp. 389–406). Cambridge, UK: Cambridge University Press.

Rabins, P. V., Merchant, A., & Nestadt, G. (1984). Criteria for diagnosing reversible dementia caused by depression: Validation by a two-year follow-up. *British Journal of Psychiatry, 144,* 488–492.

Raphael, B., Meldrum, L., & McFarlane, A. (1995). Does debriefing after psychological trauma help? (Editorial). *British Medical Journal, 310,* 1479–1480.

Raphael, B., & Wilson, J. P. (Eds.). (2000). *Psychological debriefing.* Cambridge, UK: Cambridge University Press.

Rauch, S. L., van der Kolk, B. A., Fisler, R., Alpert, N., Orr, S., Savage, C., Jenike, M., & Pitman, R. (1996). A symptom provocation study using positron emission tomography and script-driven imagery. *Archives of General Psychiatry, 53,* 380–387.

Reid, A. H. (1997). Mental handicap or learning disability? A critique of political correctness (Editorial). *British Journal of Psychiatry, 170* (1), 1.

Robinson, R. G., Starr, L. B., Kubos, K. L., Lipsey, J. R., Rao, K., & Price, T. B. (1985). A two-year longitudinal study of mood disorder following stroke: Prevalence and duration at six months follow-up. *British Journal of Psychiatry, 144,* 327–333.

Rogawski, A. S. (1982). Current status of brief psychotherapy. *Bulletin of the Menninger Clinic, 46* (4), 331–351.

Rounsaville, B. J., Dolinsky, Z. S., Babor, T. J., & Meyer, R. E. (1987). Psychopathology as a predictor of treatment outcome in alcoholics. *Archives of General Psychiatry, 44,* 505–513.

Safilios-Rothschild, C. (1970). *The sociology and social psychology of disability and rehabilitation.* New York: Random House, 149–150.

Scholes, P. (1947). Pitch. In *Oxford companion to music* (p. 731). Oxford: Oxford University Press.

Sekeles, C. (1999). Working through loss and mourning in music therapy. In T. Wigram & J. de Backer (Eds.), *Clinical applications of music therapy in psychiatry* (pp. 176–196). London: Jessica Kingsley.

Shalev, A. S., Hermesh, H., & Munitz, H. (1989). Mortality from neuroleptic malignant syndrome. *Journal of Clinical Psychiatry, 50,* 18–25.

Shapiro, F. (1998, April). Eye-movement desensitization and reprocessing. *Audio-Digest Psychiatry, 27*(7).

Solomon, S. D., Gerrity, E. T., & Muff, A. M. (1992). Efficacy of treatment for posttraumatic stress disorder: An empirical review. *JAMA, 268,* 633–635.

Stack, S., Gundlach, J., & Reeves, J. L. (1994). The heavy metal sub-culture and suicide. *Suicide and Life-Threatening Behavior, 21*(1), 15–23.

Stafford-Clark, D. (1963). *Psychiatry today.* Harmondsworth, UK: Penguin Books.

Stige, B. (1999). The meaning of music—From the client's perspective. In T. Wigram & J. de Backer (Eds.), *Clinical applications of music therapy in psychiatry* (pp. 61–83). London: Jessica Kingsley.

Stolley, J. M., Buckwalter, K., & Koenig, H. (1999). Prayer and religious coping for caregivers or persons with Alzheimer's disease. *American Journal of Alzheimer's Disease, 14*(3), 181–191.

Stone, M. H. (1989). Individual psychotherapy with victims of incest. *Psychiatric Clinics of North America, 12*(2), 237–254.

Storr, M. (1992). *Music and the mind.* London: HarperCollins.

Thaper, A., Gottesman, I. J., Owen, J., O'Donovan, M. C., & McGuffin, P. (1994). The genetics of mental retardation. *British Journal of Psychiatry, 164,* 747–758.

Treadway, R. G. (1990). Tarasoff in the therapeutic setting. *Hospital and Community Psychiatry, 41*(1), 80–81.

Tuttman, S. (1998). Protecting the therapeutic alliance in this time of changing health-care delivery systems. *International Journal of Group Psychotherapy, 47*(1), 3–16.

Twycross, R. G. (1980). The relief of pain. In C. Saunders (Ed.), *The management of terminal illness* (pp. 65–92). London: Arnold.

Twycross, R. G. (1988). Optimal pharmacological control of chronic cancer pain. *Recent Results in Cancer Research, 108,* 9–17.

Vaillant, G. E. (1977). *Adaptation to life.* Boston. Little, Brown and Co.

Vaillant, G. E. (1983). *The natural history of alcoholism.* Cambridge, MA: Harvard University Press.

van der Kolk, B. A. (1989). The treatment of victims of sexual abuse. *Psychiatric Clinics of North America, 12*(2), 389–411.

van der Kolk, B. A. (1997). The psychobiology of posttraumatic stress disorder. *Journal of Clinical Psychiatry, 56* (Suppl. 9), 16–24.

van der Kolk, B. A. (1998). The psychology and psychobiology of developmental trauma. In A. Stoudemire (Ed.), *Human behavior: An introduction for medical students* (pp. 383–399). New York: Lippincott.

van der Kolk, B. A., & van der Hart, O. (1991). The intrusive past: The flexibility of memory and the engraving of trauma. A review of thinking on difficult memories. *American Image, 48*(4), 425–454.

Walsh, K. W. (1978). *Neuropsychology: A clinical approach.* London: Churchill Livingstone.

Wegner, D. M., Broome, A., & Blomberg, S. J. (1997). Ironic effects of trying to relax under stress. *Behaviour Research and Therapy, 26*(1), 11–22.

Wheeler, B. L. (1995). *Music therapy research: Quantitative and qualitative perspectives.* Phoenixville, PA: Barcelona Publishing.

Wheeler, B. L. (1999). Experiencing pleasure in working with severely disabled children. *Journal of Music Therapy, 36*(1), 56–80.

Wolberg, L. R. (1977). *The techniques of psychotherapy.* New York: Grune and Stratton.

World Health Organisation (1980). *Classification of impairment, disability, and handicap: A manual of classification according to the consequences of disease.* Geneva: Author.

World Health Organisation (1992). *The ICD-10 classification of mental and behavioural disorders.* Geneva: Author.

Wright, B. (1960). *Physical disability: A psychological approach.* New York: Harper and Row.

Zangwill, O. L. (1987). Hermann Ebbinghaus. In R. L. Gregory (Ed.), *The Oxford companion to the mind,* (p. 207). Oxford: Oxford University Press.

Bibliography

Music Resources

Signorelli, R. (Ed.). (1998). *Exploring our world with song: A multicultural songbook.* Sydney, Australia: Uniting Church Homes and Community Services, 1 Wetherill Street, Leichard NSW 2040.

This book has the words in the original language and in an English translation. It is available in words-only and words-and-music editions.

1001 hit tunes. (1974). Sydney, Australia: Alberts Music.

Ulverscroft large print songbooks. (1967, 1987). Leicester, UK: Ulverscroft.

There are two different books available. They come in words-only and words-and-music editions.

The ultimate fake book. (1981). New York: Hal Leonard.

There are several books on different themes in the Readers Digest series, with interesting information about the songs and their composers or performers.

See also the catalogue of items published by MMB Music, St. Louis, MO, for musical books and for textbooks. MMB's address is at the front of this book.

The wide-ranging books published by Jessica Kingsley provide useful reading for music therapists. Catalogues from: 116 Pentonville Road, London N1 9JB UK, and 1900 Frost Road, Suite 101, Boston, PA 19007 USA.

Recommended Books and Journals

Suggestion Regarding Journals

These lists are by no means complete. Much depends on the availability of any journal in the therapist's geographical location and the publications to which the employing facility subscribes.

Since it is impossible for any individual therapist to read in detail each and every journal suggested here, it is helpful to ask your hospital librarian to put you on the circulation list for indices of appropriate publications. It takes only a few moments to read these and see whether there are articles that are relevant to your own particular area of work.

General Texts on Palliative and Terminal Care

Hinton, J. (1967). *Dying.* Harmondsworth, UK: Penguin Books.

Kubler Ross, E. (1974). *Questions and answers on death and dying.* New York: Macmillan Publishing.

Parkes, C. M. (1978). *Bereavement: Studies in adult grief.* Harmondsworth, UK: Penguin Books.

Saunders, C. (Ed.). (1990). *Hospice and palliative care: An interdisciplinary approach.* London: Edward Arnold.

This book is based on work at St. Christopher's Hospice, London, a hospice that cares for people with long-term conditions such as upper motor neurone disease and is not restricted to cancer patients. The book includes an interesting chapter on the causes and hazards of staff splitting.

Worden, W. (1983). *Grief counselling and grief therapy.* London: Tavistock. (Original work published in 1982. New York: Springfield.)

General Psychiatry and Forensic Psychiatry

Books

Chiu, E., & Ames, D. (Eds.). (1994). *Functional psychiatric disorders of the elderly.* Cambridge, UK: Cambridge University Press.

Cox, M. (1988). *Coding the therapeutic process: Emblems of encounter: A manual for therapists and counsellors.* London: Jessica Kingsley.

Cox, M. (1988). *Structuring the therapeutic process: Compromise with chaos: The therapist's response to the individual and the group* (2nd ed.). London: Jessica Kingsley.

Cox, M. (1992). *Shakespeare comes to Broadmoor: The actors are come hither: The performance of tragedy in a secure psychiatric hospital.* London: Jessica Kingsley.

This book is an extraordinary account of an extraordinary event and the positive, valuable impact the play had upon patients in this forensic psychiatric hospital.

Gabbard, G. O. (1994). *Psychodynamic psychiatry in clinical practice: The DSM-IV edition.* Washington, DC: American Psychiatric Association.

Gelder, M., Gath, D., Mayou, R., & Cowen, P. (Eds.). (1996). *The Oxford textbook of psychiatry.* Oxford: Oxford University Press.

Jacoby, R., & Oppenheimer, C. (Eds.). (1991). *Psychiatry in the elderly.* Oxford: Oxford University Press.

Lafond, V. (1994). *Grieving mental illness: A guide for patients and their caregivers.* Toronto: University of Toronto Press.

Psychiatric Clinics of North America

Note that all serials entitled ——— *Clinics of North America*, of which there are many, are published as hardback books, but are usually stored on library shelves in the section set aside for journals.

Journals

American Journal of Psychiatry
Archives of General Psychiatry
Australasian Psychiatry
Australia & New Zealand Journal of Psychiatry
British Journal of Psychiatry
Bulletin of the Menninger Clinic
Canadian Journal of Psychiatry
*Current Opinion in Psychiatry**
Hospital and Community Psychiatry
Psychiatric Clinics of North America

Geriatrics

Books

Bright. R. (1990). *Why does THAT happen?* Wahroonga, Australia: Music Therapy Enterprises.

This is a dictionary-style book on disorders and disabilities in old age, with some emphasis on the point of view of the music therapist.

Bright, R. (1997). *Wholeness in later life.* London: Jessica Kingsley.

This book gives a positive approach to aging, and is unusual in discussing the special needs in later life of those who have had lifelong disabilities.

Mace, N., & Rabins, P. (1991). *The thirty-six hour day.* Baltimore, MD: Johns Hopkins Press.

The name reflects the exhaustion of caregivers and enhances the professional's understanding of the difficulties faced by carers of people with dementing illness.

Newton, E. (1979). *This bed my centre.* Melbourne, Australia: McPhee-Gribble.

A personal response to disability and discrimination in later life.

*Note that any journal with "Current Opinion in..." as part of its title is a review journal, which republishes and discusses major papers from standard journals, on particular topics in a given field (such as psychiatry, anaesthetics, and so on.) There are usually only one or two topics per issue, and each article is marked with its importance by a given number of asterisks, depending upon its perceived importance for the professional.

Sherman, B. (1999). *Dementia with dignity* (2nd ed.). New York: McGraw-Hill.

Particularly helpful because it is, as the author says, about people rather than about illness!

Sokalovsky, J. (Ed.). (1990). *The cultural context of aging.* New York: Bergin and Garvey.

Journals

Age and Ageing
American Journal of Alzheimer's Disease (and related disorders)
Australasian Journal on Ageing
Clinics in Geriatric Medicine
International Journal of Geriatric Psychiatry
Journal of Dementia Care
Journal of the American Geriatrics Society
Stroke

General Disabilities and Rehabilitation

Books

Neurologic clinics of North America

As with other serials published as ——— *Clinics of North America,* each issue deals with a particular topic or a specific disorder, with selected articles by various specialists. Many of these are relevant to rehabilitation.

Werner-Belard, J. (1980). *Grief responses to long-term illness and disability.* Reston, VA: Reston.

This is a helpful book providing insights into the emotional and other responses of those who have become impaired and handicapped by illness or accident, and of their families, as they adapt to rehabilitation and to their changed circumstances and relationships.

Whiteneck, G., Charlifue, et al. (Eds.) (1993). *Aging with a spinal cord injury.* New York: Demos.

Different chapters by different writers, reflecting a wide range of aspects of the subject.

Wright, B. (1960). *Physical disability: A psychological approach.* New York: Harper and Row.

Despite the time that has passed since this book was written, it remains an irreplaceable source of understanding about people's responses to disability.

Journals

Archives of Physical Medicine and Rehabilitation
American Journal of Physical Medicine and Rehabilitation

General Texts on Aspects of Grief

Books

Bright, R., (1986). *Grieving: A handbook for those who care.* St. Louis, MO: MMB Music.

Bright, R. (1996). *Grief and powerlessness.* London: Jessica Kingsley.

Bright, R. (1997). *Wholeness in later life.* London: Jessica Kingsley.

Doka, K. (1989). *Disenfranchised grief.* Lexington, MA: Lexington Books.

This book discusses the forbidden griefs, the situations in which grief must be hidden or repressed because of a variety of circumstances, and the effects of this on the individual.

Raphael, B., & Wilson, J. P. (Eds.). (2000). *Psychological debriefing.* Cambridge, UK: Cambridge University Press.

This book is essential reading for all therapists and counselors. Various authors discuss "de-briefing"—the reasons for its continuing popularity, its possible benefits, and potential risks—and also describe and discuss other processes including the management of critical incidents and the management of stress.

Journals

British Medical Journal
JAMA (previously called *Journal of the American Medical Association*)
New England Journal of Medicine
The Lancet

Name Index

D

E

F

G

H

I

J

K

Subject Index